ANGUISHED MEN OF GOD

Books by Wesley Shrader

DEAR CHARLES

THE LONG ARM OF GOD

OF MEN AND ANGELS

YESHUA'S DIARY

COLLEGE RUINED OUR DAUGHTER

ANGUISHED MEN OF GOD

ANGUISHED MEN OF GOD

WESLEY SHRADER

1817

HARPER & ROW, PUBLISHERS

NEW YORK, EVANSTON, AND LONDON

TO DOUG AND DON

who survived life in the parsonage

CONTENTS

CONTENTS

Part II *Finding the Light*

CONTENTS

PREFACE

Many people both within and outside of the church are baffled by the strange behavior of today's parish ministers. In this book I have attempted to describe this behavior in some detail and to offer an explanation of why they act as they do. By strange behavior I do not refer to changing ministerial manners and style—long hair, heavy sideburns, and colorful clothes; nor am I interested primarily in the "activist" minister whose motto in these days appears to have become "Are you picketing with me, Jesus?" I am here dealing with ministers who are attempting to change the public image of the preacher, and more importantly with those who are determined to destroy the structure of today's organized church so that their children will not recognize what today exists as "the church."

In recent years many clergymen, Catholic and Protestant, have found the work of the church empty, futile, and filled with unending frustration—so much so that they have left it. Untold numbers remain within their calling, but day by day they perform their duties mechanically and with little enthusiasm. In *Anguished Men of God* I describe the life and ministry of certain clergymen who struggle with the "organized" church, but who in different ways ultimately find truth and meaning in what they are doing. Thus, I have put on paper my own beliefs (and hopes) concerning the direction I feel tomorrow's church and ministry will take.

In telling this story I have deliberately chosen the device of letter-writing. I am convinced that through the medium of letters one can achieve a warmth and intimacy surpassing that of any other literary form including that of the novel or drama. This is my third book of letters. The other two are *Dear Charles* (letters to a young minister) and *College Ruined Our Daughter* (letters to anxious parents of college students).

I suggest that readers not make the mistake of skipping from one section of the book to another but read the story from beginning to end. Motivation, characterization, conflicts and resolution, can only come alive when this is done.

In creating the characters of the Reverend Thomas Emerson Jones and Father Sean O'Malley, I must not leave the impression that either one is typical of the pastors in his respective communion. I can only say that to me they are real, terribly real, perhaps because in my own life as a parish minister I have embodied a little of each.

Wesley Shrader
New York City

Part I

MAKING THE BREAK

A *Voice from the Past*

Dear Sean,

My God, how great to hear from you!

How long has it been—four years? Five years? It seems even longer. You just dropped from sight. I incorrectly got the word that you had been sent to Brazil. All these months and years I kept hoping to get a note or a letter but there was nothing but silence. Now that you're back in the States, perhaps we can get together—though California is farther from the East Coast than Puerto Rico.

I have a thousand questions, and since you ask about what has been going on in this part of the world perhaps we can fill each other in. I'm still stuck in Briar Wood, still pastor of the (God help me) Lawrence A. Vandergrift, Sr. Presbyterian Church. This is my twelfth year. Since I'm now forty-six, the chances of being called to another church are indeed dim. In the past several years I've had several nibbles and two firm invitations to other pastorates, but each one presented less opportunity than what I have. Now it's too late. Attractive churches in my denomination rarely call men past forty-five. Tall, handsome, toothy men, with hair, between thirty and forty, are in demand, especially those who have played ball with the establishment and have raised considerable money for denominational causes. As you can guess, I am still at odds with the bureaucrats who run our denomination. Organized, institutional religion is getting harder and harder for me to take.

You ask about several old friends. The ecumenical foursome broke up shortly after you departed. Julian Feldman left the rabbinate. He got a job as a reporter for the *Grovetown News* in Connecticut, one of the really influential newspapers in New England. He was soon made assistant editor, then associate editor, and now he is senior editor and going great guns. Well, you know Julian—he was the brains of our crowd. But he not only had brains; he demonstrated more than once that he had integrity. As the men of the official board at Beth Israel learned the hard way.

Allen McCall is still smooth, handsome, and glib. He has just recently been moved or transferred (whatever the Methodists do) to a large church on the mainline near Philadelphia. He wrote me that his church has three thousand members, he has a staff of twelve professionals working with him, and his starting salary—not including all the benefits— is $25,000. He is still a man who instinctively knows what people want to hear and delivers it with great ability.

I've given up on golf. When you left, Monday afternoons at the course were something of a drag. I now keep my nose to the grindstone seven days a week. Speaking of golf, remember how I could beat both you and Julian, and both of you consistently beat Allen but I never could? I've become pretty much of a loner in Briar Wood. I don't really like being so much alone, but since there is no one, especially among the clergy, whose company I enjoy I suppose I'll keep it this way.

Perhaps the next time you write you can give me some details of your ups and downs these past five years. I knew you were in serious trouble when you went on television and charged your bishop with being a racist (which everybody knew he was). Allen said at the time you were a fool. "Why do men like Sean think they have to save the world?" Of course, you know his position. The race question can't be solved in a day; blacks are moving too fast, and the less today's clergyman says about the problem the better off he'll be. Allen tackled me last year in much the same manner for my denunciation of our involvement in Vietnam. He simply does not get the point of sticking your neck out or risking your future.

Now to answer the question which no doubt prompted your letter to me—what has become of Marie. Within weeks after your attack on the bishop and your sudden and mysterious exit from the country, Marie renounced the habit; she is no longer a nun. She went to New York, took a position as instructor (sociology, I think) at Columbia. There she met and eventually fell in love with a professor, head of her department. He is divorced and the father of two teen-age sons. They were married, and now have a little boy.

Early this year I attended a conference at Columbia and saw her in the early months of her pregnancy. She was radiant and as beautiful as ever. With no hesitation or embarrassment she asked if I had had any word from you. Of course I hadn't. I hope the news about her being married doesn't upset you. My guess is, you may be leaving the priesthood now—but five years is a long time for a girl to wait.

My curiosity knows no bounds. If you are in a position to do so, please let me know why you were sent to Puerto Rico and why you were shipped back to the States.

I shall be waiting to hear from you.

Tom

Love Is What It Was

Dear Tom,

Your letter is deeply appreciated. All the more because I
know you are busy, while I have time on my hands. I owe you
an apology. There was really no excuse for my leaving Briar
Wood as I did—except that I was in such an emotional state
that I could not force myself to talk to anyone. My recent
letter to you was written primarily for the reason you de-
tected. I was and am concerned to know what has happened
to Marie. However, please don't think this is the only reason
I wrote. I have an abiding affection for you and your family.
Actually you and your wife and children are the only
"family" I have in this part of the world. My mother and
father and two sisters are still living on the farm outside of
Dublin. My younger brother, Tim, is the owner and principal
of a private school in Hong Kong. So I feel somewhat dependent on the Jones family. And I was indeed interested to know
what had happened to Julian and Allen.

Let me clear up one thing: my leaving Briar Wood as I did
was prompted by two events, both of them shattering. Differ-
ences with the hierarchy, including the Bishop, came to a
head the week of the now famous television program. Also,
my relations with Marie reached an impasse at the same time.
The simple friendship we had from the time she came to
teach at St. Elizabeth's had deepened into love. She had
resolved to leave her Order at the end of the school year. I
was to make the break at the same time. We planned to be
married in June, after giving great care and thought to our
contemplated action. You know me almost as well as I know
myself. I make decisions only after every possibility has been
exhausted. I suppose ordinarily you could call this my conservative streak.

The day before I left Briar Wood, I was notified that my
Bishop was "lending" me to the Bishop of Puerto Rico on

6

temporary assignment, for two reasons. He was known as a man of strong views who would tolerate no nonsense from an upstart priest. And Puerto Rico has no race problem. The word was out among the brothers that I was being sent to Brazil, and I was requested to tell no one in the States that my destination was Puerto Rico. I suppose I should have called you or written you at least that I was leaving, but I was broken and depressed and simply didn't do it. Can you forgive me?

That same night Marie and I met in her home near Princeton. Her parents (who never approved of her becoming a nun) were in Europe. The dogwood was in bloom and the countryside was peacefully beautiful. We sat down to a simple meal she had prepared. A bottle of wine helped make the conversation easier. We had discussed several times before, of course, the two major points around which our decisions revolved: the break with the Church and our marriage. We had many interests and values in common; we both felt we needed and wanted marriage, even at the price of separation from the Church. At the time, Marie was twenty-nine and I thirty-five. We were not teen-agers, and up to that moment we thought we knew what we were doing.

To make a long story very short, and without going into details, I admitted to her my realization that our future together as man and wife could never be. I could not sacrifice the priesthood, my supreme calling in life. To my surprise, she agreed with me. With tears in her eyes she said, "With some other man it might have been—but not with you, Sean O'Malley—you are a priest forever." I left without telling her when I was leaving Briar Wood or where I was being sent. Now she is married and has a child. I can only say I am happy for her. Under no circumstances will I ever write her or in any way get in touch with her. And certainly I myself would not risk seeing her again.

I want to hear about your work and your home—Grace and

the children. Tom, Jr. was sixteen when I left. Gail was the baby—I assume there are still four. From the tone of your last letter you are still fighting the establishment, and I take it this means both religious and political. For the time being I am holed up in one of our better retreat centers in southern California, not too far from San Diego. I have little to do except pray, relax, and read. In the meantime, I'm hungry for news. Tell me about Julian and his life since he left Beth Israel. I always liked and respected him. He was a real man. And Allen—I can see him now, Cadillac and all! Somehow I feel he has gone to the place so beautifully prepared for him. Your comments about our foursome are amusing. You could beat both Julian and me because playing against us you were relaxed. With Allen you were as tense as if your life depended on it.

Keep in touch. God bless you.

Sean

P.S. Whatever happened to the Smoketown Community Center we worked so hard to bring into being? Did it just die aborning, or has it survived white racism and black power?

SECTION TWO

There Are *Reasons*

Dear Sean,

You did not need to apologize, either for leaving the community or for writing to me out of a secondary motive. In the circumstances, I would have done the same thing. Of course, I knew your friendship with Sister Marie had become serious. I thought for sure that you would leave the priesthood and marry her, and I was hoping you would.

So—you are a priest, and so you will remain! It is ironic that you should write at this particular time. Early this year I myself made the decision to leave the ministry and find some other means of support. I've been a parish minister for twenty years, and have endured all the humiliation and frustration I can take.

Julian found he could no longer function as a rabbi. His two principal reasons apply equally to me. The organized, institutional church is totally irrelevant to the day in which we live. Racism is rampant in the country and the church has been the last organization to deal with it; the war in Vietnam is more meaningless than ever, and the church has hardly lifted its voice in protest. In fact, many lay people and ministers alike are critical of those who openly register any sort of protest. Young people across the country are in a state of rebellion. Instead of trying to discover the reasons for the rebellion, church people demand more discipline and more punishment. Services of worship are couched in language and forms of the Middle Ages; Sunday-school instruction, even for high-school young people, goes barely beyond the seventh or eighth grades. Puritanical morality rooted in eighteen- and nineteenth-century religion still dominates the church today.

Julian also left the rabbinate because of certain restrictions on his freedom. Beth Israel did not provide him with a free forum. As you know, this particular synagogue had grown from a small congregation to one of the most influential in the East. The members are affluent and upper-middle-class— remember when the Green Tree Country Club refused to admit Jews, and the leading members of Beth Israel bought the club?

Julian got into serious difficulty with his official board over

Vietnam. Of course he was radically against our involvement. From the very beginning of the massive build-up, he publicly opposed our efforts. He viewed the conflict as a civil war between Vietnamese people and looked with horror upon our almost unlimited backing of a succession of dictatorlike regimes which could muster small political support from their own people. He preached a sermon in which he said, "Millions of American dollars are being syphoned off by South Vietnam's political and military leaders." Julian said further that if our treaty commitments to SEATO, and more especially to South Vietnam, involved vast economic support, then to support corrupt political machines was more dishonest than to break the treaty. He would not accept the domino theory or swallow the idea that the existence and security of the United States were threatened.

So from his pulpit he protested. All hell broke loose. He was called on the carpet by his official board. They told him in plain words to cool it or find another synagogue. Get this: *not* because the membership disagreed with his position on Vietnam. The board's point was that Jews in Briar Wood had struggled long and hard for community acceptance. Now that they had arrived, they would not let the rabbi destroy their position! If he remained as their rabbi, he would have to keep quiet about Vietnam.

As I said, he didn't look for another synagogue; he took a job as a reporter with a salary half of what he had been making. This, with three children, one ready for college. His wife had to go to work to help pay the bills.

I am leaving the parish for the same reasons—the church is irrelevant and insensitive to the real problems of our day. The freedom of my pulpit has been threatened in precisely the same way as Julian's, and over the same issues. However, there is still a third reason for my making the break, and it involves a crisis of faith. I have been reading the death-of-God boys, and though they have been severely criticized both in the church and out of it, I am convinced that they are saying something genuine. God for me is dead. In fact, I doubt that the God of love, care, and compassion about whom I have been preaching all these years ever existed! If He exists, why does He not say something or do something when the people of this creation need Him? He neither speaks nor acts for the simple reason that He is dead. Next September I'm checking out. Grace knows about my decision, but the children as yet do not. As far as I know, no one in my church or on my official board knows. Since you have made the decision to stay in the priesthood, I thought it would be paradoxically interesting if I let you know my plans for leaving.

I'll try to tell you later, in another letter, some of the tragic and ludicrous experiences I've had since making the decision to get out. "Dislocated" priests think they are the only ones who have trouble getting relocated. I can assure you it's no bed of roses for a forty-six-year-old Protestant minister with four kids.

You asked about the Smoketown Community Center. It has survived! A young woman, graduate of Howard University, is the director and she's doing a great job. Thus far neither white racism nor black power has been able to defeat its integrated program. The center almost went under until I appealed to my church to save it. They agreed to help, on one condition. On the lot adjacent to the center a Presbyterian chapel—Smoketown Presbyterian Chapel—must be erected. This has been done, and both center and chapel have flourished. The chapel is now ready to be taken into the presbytery as a full-fledged church, half-white and half-black!

I'm anxious to hear more about your life at Santa Bella. Write soon!

Tom

11

When God Calls

Dear Tom,

It was with regret that I learned your decision to leave the ministry. The divine call to the religious life as a servant-leader of God's people is no insignificant matter. There is no doubt in my mind that God calls a man to a certain type of work. In my case this was (and still is) the most vivid experience of my life. The call came shortly after my first Communion, though I did not make it known until I was fifteen. No parent, no priest or sister pressed me toward the holy vocation. I responded to the call, and I consider being a priest the greatest honor of my life. The only time I was ever tempted to leave the priesthood was during my time at Briar Wood, when the pressures of the hierarchy and my love for Marie combined to make me doubt my calling. Since then, though I have often been unhappy, I have never doubted the rightness of my decision to remain in the Church.

Concerning your sympathy with the death-of-God theologians, all I can say is, this is not the Tom Jones I know. Within that breezy, boisterous nature of yours is a man who knows God and cares deeply about the things of God. In your case I predict there will be a more wonderful resurrection of the divine. Death-of-God? "This, too, shall pass away."

You ask about the events that led to my being in California and want to know if I am in jail or on a real retreat. The story of my leaving Puerto Rico is a long one, and perhaps when I get a chance I can relate it to you. I am not in jail—I'm at Santa Bella, a retreat center for priests who need various types of instruction and assistance. Men with serious sex problems, alcoholics, or those with sticky fingers for money are here for rest, meditation, observation, and (hopefully) rehabilitation. I am the only one whose main difficulty is the inability to live with the hierarchy. Eventually I will be examined by fellow priests, physicians, and psychiatrists. After several months of "treatment," there will be a conference with the Father Superior, who will make the decision concerning my future. I wish it were tomorrow—I'm not used to the quiet life and want only to be sent to a parish where I can do God's work.

By courteous request I am confined at Santa Bella. Since I am under suspension, I can attend Mass but cannot say Mass —and there is a big difference. I am privileged to write and receive letters and have reason to believe the mail is not censored. Aside from the breviary and the missal, my reading is restricted to certain areas. I will be required to read and pass tests on seven books. You'll be interested in the titles: *Famous Conversions to Catholicism, The Meaning of Infallibility, The Social Conscience of the Catholic Church, A Catholic Rationale for Censorship, The Misdeeds of Martin Luther, The Humanitarianism of Paul VI, The Vow of Obedience.*

Of course there are no secular newspapers, magazines, radios, or TV sets here. My only contact with the outside world is the link I have with you and limited conversations with the priests who pass through these doors.

As far as I can recall, I never told you about the events that led to the now famous television program, when in answer to a commentator's question I said, "My Bishop is a racist." When I came to St. Elizabeth's more than ten years ago I was put in charge of the school—Grades 1-12—and, since my background is Latin-American studies, I taught one high-school class in the religious and political structures of Central America and an advanced class in Spanish. It was not long before I was in serious difficulty with Father O'Connell, my immediate superior in the parish. He seemed to me to be out of touch with the times. Our school, all grades, had approximately 1,200 pupils and a large number of nuns and lay teachers. Many parochial schools were in serious financial trouble, but not St. Elizabeth's. Upper-middle-class Catholics in the area proudly saw to that. The race problem at that time was beginning to boil. We were a hundred per cent white, and I insisted that Negro children applying for admission for the next school year must be admitted. If they were from the ghetto of Smoketown and disadvantaged, we should provide scholarships for them. My dear pastor vetoed each and every decision I made in this direction. At last he reported me to the Bishop, who called me to New Lake. There I heard the precise words that Julian heard from his official board. St. Elizabeth was solvent because it had remained white. Catholics had struggled hard to be accepted in an affluent Protestant community. The Bishop agreed wholeheartedly with Father O'Connell. He threatened me with suspension if I continued to agitate for an integrated school. I returned to Briar Wood grim and determined. Within weeks I ordered three Negro children admitted to the lower grades and one to high school. The pastor, the Bishop, and I met head on— we had a confrontation. I was told to be ready to leave for Puerto Rico immediately. It was at this point that, by coincidence, I went on the television panel show, and in answer to the commentator's question about the racial views of the Bishop described him as a racist. (I have since learned that the Bishop was in contact with the Vatican concerning my case. It was the Vatican that gave the order for me to be sent to Puerto Rico.)

I was then forced to make the decision of my life. The relationship between Marie and myself had reached the crucial stage. We planned to marry. You know the rest of the story.

I have heard that a number of our mutual friends, both priests and ministers, have left the Church. If you know where any of them are, please let me have this information.

Sean

SECTION THREE

That Was the Year That Was

Dear Sean,

It pleases me to learn that though your confinement is tedious, in some ways it is pleasant. At least there is a chance for rest and relaxation. The authorities are apparently trying to make up their minds what to do with you. In my judgment the Church does not know, any more than the world does, how to deal with a man intent on living the life of love. This is one of the reasons why I think the institutional church and the professional ministry have had it. Phillips Brooks once said, "The Christian ministry is the largest field for the growth of the human soul that this world offers." He must have been out of his mind. I agree with Rev. George Caleb Moor, a famous Baptist minister of another generation, who said concerning the ministry that the minister must have

> the strength of an ox,
> the tenacity of a bulldog,
> the daring of a lion,
> the patience of a jackass,
> the industry of a beaver,
> the versatility of a chameleon,
> the vision of an eagle,
> the melodies of a nightingale,
> the hide of a rhinoceros,
> the disposition of an angel,
> the resignation of an incurable, and
> the loyalty of an apostle.

Where is the man who measures up?

I recently ran across an excerpt of a speech you delivered

before the Briar Wood Sinoki Club in 1959. I was present that day and took notes. I send these excerpts to reemphasize the point that neither the Church nor the community will long tolerate a prophet.

Gentlemen:
I speak to you today on "The Unfaced and Unrecognizable Race Problem in Our Community." On the south side of our city the ghetto of Smoketown, with its misery and disease, its open sewers and rat-infested tenements, stands as a silent judgment on our way of life. By subtle and open practices of discrimination, we have sealed these people off from the main stream of community life and have successfully kept them in their places. We have denied their children an education, we have restricted their opportunities for employment, but most serious of all, property owners in cooperation with local real estate brokers have found ways of perpetuating the ghetto and preventing the purchase of homes in a decent neighborhood. This type of discrimination applies to all voluntary organizations in our community, the country club, women's clubs, civic clubs such as Sinoki, private schools, and even churches.

Our political leaders have told you what you most want to hear: that the black man is satisfied with his lot in life, he does not want "out," he is lazy and unambitious, and his conduct, both public and private, is disgracefully immoral. These leaders have further charged that if certain priests and ministers would keep their mouths shut about the "horrors" of racism there would be no problem in Briar Wood.

Gentlemen, I tell you that, in this year of Our Lord 1959, we are sitting on an active volcano which within a few short years will erupt. When this occurs our cities will burn, riots will be the order of the day, crime on the streets will multiply. The fears of white people will surface, and in their panic they (who hold police and military power) will demand of government leaders greater punishment and disciplinary action, but then it will be too late. The black man will have decided that he has little to lose, and that if he cannot have the good things of American life for himself and his family, no one will have them. We will have in this country two separated societies

16

created by fear and hate and perpetuated by force and violence. Our beautiful parks will stand silent and idle, our streets after dark will be empty and our homes padlocked. You, your children, and your grandchildren will live in terror. Men of Sinoki, business and political leaders of our community, I plead with you—I beg you in the name of justice to break the shackles of servitude of our black brothers. Let these people go—help them out of their misery.

The men of Sinoki were stunned that day. They were confronted with their motto, "Service Before Self." Did this motto really mean honesty and justice only for "our kind" or did it include the untouchables? It showed great restraint that the members did not mob you that day. This was the first and only time I ever saw a Sinoki meeting hurriedly dismissed without so much as a reference to the speaker or his address.

Well, Sean, you were more than prophetic. White people would not voluntarily let them "out." We now have a nightmare on our hands. Riots and the destruction of our cities have taken place from Los Angeles to Philadelphia and many angry spots in between. White people live in fear, and still they ask, "Why do black people act like that?"

What a blessed year was 1959! We had piety on the Potomac, no big wars (except the cold war), the President went to church every Sunday and to prayer breakfasts during the week. Bishop Sheen, Billy Graham, and Norman Vincent Peale were the spokesmen for religion in America. White people laughed, sang, made money, and kept the Negro in his place. But he, the black man, smoldering in hate, lay in his crowded tenements and plotted the destruction of a system that would not take him in.

I would like to be able to give you the names and addresses of your friends who have recently left the Church, but I'm afraid I can't be of much help. Fathers Clasky, Giappi, and Romana are now working at secular jobs in New York. Two of them are with the poverty program. Father Daniel and

17

Father Justina are among the large number of priests recently suspended in Washington over the birth control issue. As yet, though suspended, they have not left the Church. All five of the nuns who taught with Sister Marie at St. Elizabeth's have left the order. The last I heard, three of them were married. The convent to which they were attached in Montville has been closed.

We also have had quite a shake-up among the Protestant clergy. Remember Bill Myers, Episcopal rector in Bay View? He's now selling insurance. Ross Neighbors, Methodist, is teaching in a high school near Harrisburg. Bob Hemsley, Lutheran, left his church and is working for the poverty program. Bob has severed all relations with the church and never attends. My fellow Presbyterian, Charles Moore, a great guy—remember, we used to go to the Rathskeller with him?—is now a copy writer for NBC. Leonard Beers, Baptist (formerly of the faculty at Colgate-Rochester), is practicing law. He had two years of law before entering the ministry. You may be surprised to hear me say this, but truth is truth: *every one* of my Protestant clergy friends past forty would leave the parish ministry tomorrow, if family obligations did not hold them, and if they could make the right connection in the outside world.

Best of luck,

Tom

A Little Thing Called Sex

Dear Tom,

Thanks for the notes on the Sinoki speech. Perhaps courage at that time was the way of the fool. At any rate, 1959 was a good and peaceful year for white America. I need no longer keep the inspiration of that speech a secret. Several months before that I had a private conference, man to man, with Malcolm X in New York. We talked for five hours. That was the first time I really sensed the hatred of the black man for this society. In making the speech to the civic club I was doing something I simply had to do.

You ask about my work in Puerto Rico. On my arrival in the Commonwealth, I was assigned as one of four assistant pastors of the Most Holy Virgin Catholic Church in San Juan. I found there a more progressive and enlightened clergy than in the States. The burning issue at the time was birth control. I had long since made up my mind that the use of contraceptives by a married couple was a matter of conscience and not a concern of the Church. When a frightened Puerto Rican woman came to confession stating that she or her Catholic husband had used a contraceptive, I told her this was not a sin that required confession. I was surprised to learn that all of the priests on the staff, including the old pastor, my superior, had quietly been saying the same thing for years.

I had been in touch with a number of brilliant Catholic theologians in the United States and Canada, and they assured me that my position was correct and that Pope John would soon issue an encyclical to this effect. The tragedy of the Church's present position is not simply in the population explosion which threatens to destroy civilization, but in the countless numbers of couples who go through married life fearing one more pregnancy, fearing the act of intercourse itself, fearing the confessional and the ire of the priest. The prohibition of contraceptives has probably caused more misery to Catholic couples than all other factors combined.

Just before I left Briar Wood a young man, member of our parish, came to see me for a private conference. His case is not isolated and different, it is not an exception to the rule;

19

it is the rule. He was married to a beautiful high-spirited girl about thirty. They had five children under seven, and their financial situation was desperate. He was the assistant manager of a department store. His wife could not work; she was always pregnant, and of course there were the children to be cared for. Then he told me how he and his lovely young wife tried to handle it. In the early years of their marriage, they tried the rhythm method. They did this fearfully and with little success. Babies kept coming. Then they tried the withdrawal method, and found this to be unsatisfactory as well as a sin which they had to confess. In recent months they have tried the "abstinence" method. To make continence easier, they decided on several procedures. They would not undress in each other's presence or be in the bathroom at the same time. They sold their double bed and bought twin beds. The final decision involved moving into separate bedrooms. His wife took the girls with her and he took the boys with him. Their longest period of abstinence, which they had broken the night before, was three months. "What do we do?" he cried in anguish.

"The use of contraceptives by a married couple is not a sin," I said. These were my words to a harried and desperate young man. I know I saved his marriage; I may have saved his life. The pastor, my superior in Briar Wood, never knew that I was spreading such heresy among his parishioners.

I had been in Puerto Rico only a short time when I was caught in a bitter political battle, one that rocked the country. Governor Luis Múnoz, a strong Catholic layman, not only advocated artificial means of birth control but had set up birth-control clinics from one end of the island to another. This infuriated the Most Reverend James McManus, Bishop of Puerto Rico. The Bishop distributed a pastoral letter and in the press publically stated that Catholics could not vote for Governor Múnoz. If they did so, they would be under the

20

penalty of serious sin. The Bishop's position precipitated two problems: freedom for a Catholic couple to use contraceptives and freedom to vote. The old pastor of the church and my fellow priests on the staff of the Most Holy Virgin Church were indignant at the Bishop's untenable directive, but they could not bring themselves to the point of challenging him. For my immediate superior birth control was a dead issue. He, too, had talked to a number of leading theologians and was assured that Pope John would lift the ban. But the old man said sadly, "Opposing the Bishop in Puerto Rico is suicide." I was instructed to say nothing either in public or private about the most burning issue of that day. I promptly went out into the streets to promote the candidacy of Gov. Múnoz. I personally visited all the birth-control clinics in our area and congratulated the doctors and nurses on the great and good job they were doing. However, I soon learned that the Bishop was holding my old pastor responsible for my actions, and *he* would be disciplined if he did not shut up the obstreperous priest from the States. Reluctantly I withdrew from the public battle. But you may recall that Governor Múnoz won the election by a landslide; thus the Bishop was repudiated by his own people.

This incident had nothing to do with my suspension and expulsion from Puerto Rico. In a later letter, I shall attempt to give you the details that led to my return to the States. In the meantime, you have told me nothing about Grace and the children. Truly, I want to hear about all of them.

Sean

Blessed Are the Celibates

Dear Sean,

You're not alone in the battle over birth control. That's for sure! The Pope's encylical has been issued since you were a guest at Santa Bella, but I'm sure you must have got wind of it. However, you may not be aware of the controversy it has stirred within the ranks.

Top Catholic theologians in this country, Canada, France, Holland, England, and elsewhere have spoken their piece. The Papal Commission on Birth Control approved by a 70 to 14 vote the use of any "harmless, effective contraceptive methods by married couples." A group of fifteen bishops and cardinals within the commission prepared for the Pope a statement fully endorsing the commission's position. They expected Paul VI to issue an encyclical compatible with their conclusions.

Bishop James P. Shannon, Auxiliary Bishop of St. Paul and Minneapolis recently resigned his position as Bishop over the birth-control issue. In a stinging letter to the Pope, the Bishop wrote:

> In my pastoral experience I have found that this teaching is simply impossible of observance by many faithful and generous spouses, and I cannot believe that God binds men to impossible standards. In seeking to counsel such persons I have found myself resorting to all sorts of casuistry and rationalization in the hope that I might keep faith both with Your Holiness and with the people of God who seek my help. I must now relunctantly admit that I am ashamed of the kind of advice I have given some of these people, ashamed because it has been bad theology, bad psychology and because it has not been an honest reflection of my own inner convictions.

If you are not doing any outside reading these days, you may have also missed the comment by Father Hans Küng in Switzerland. He said, "The Pope was wrong in declaring the use of contraceptives by a married couple a sin." Exactly what *you* have been saying for the past ten years!

In a public gesture of protest, Monsignor Joseph Gallagher of Baltimore renounced his title of *Monsignor*. To him the Pope's encyclical was "tragic and disastrous."

Dr. John Rock, your man at Harvard (did he not discover the pill?), said, "I was scandalized by the Pope's statement. One would hardly have expected the avowed leader of Christianity to abdicate so completely responsibility for the ultimate welfare of all." There has been a general uprising of priests in the Washington area. To date eighty-seven militant priests have signed a dissenting statement. Several of these have been suspended. So, my friend, you are not alone!

The unfortunate (or fortunate?) aspect of this controversy is that the subject of birth control is no longer the issue. The issue—and I am sure you read this as I do—involves an interpretation of the authority of the Church and the question of obedience. Who has the final word, the Church or the individual's enlightened conscience?

Several times you have asked about Grace and the family, and I have postponed replying—perhaps because I was waiting for things to get better. But they are getting worse, so I will answer. At the moment, I am on a one-man crusade for clerical celibacy! I am weary of married life and want out. (How does one get "out"—especially if he is a minister with four kids?) St. Paul was right. It is better that one who has a religious vocation remain as he was—unmarried. Marriage is no good for the man who must do the work of the Church. Every time I begin a series of sermons on "How To Have a Happy Home" or "Making a Success of Marriage," Grace and I have a knock-down, drag-out fight the results of which last for weeks. The trouble with Grace is, she is just like her

23

mother. As she gets older the likeness in both appearance and temperament increases. Since her mother has never liked me and I have never liked her, this has posed a problem.

I suppose I should be more understanding with Grace. She is going through the change of life, and for many women this is a difficult time. She is no longer sweet and loving, but touchy, irritable, and explosive. So I am all for clerical celibacy. I still like (and need) sex, especially on Saturday night to calm me down, but at forty-six I think I could now live without it.

The children? It is difficult for me to write about them, especially Tom, Jr. Since he was a little fellow, he has been the apple of my eye and the very heart of my life. I didn't particularly care what line of work he pursued or what profession he followed, I just wanted him to be a person, a real honest-to-God man. He was a junior at Princeton, and without even consulting us he dropped out of college (an *A* student) and enlisted in the Army. He wanted to fight in Vietnam. His views are the very opposite of mine. The domino theory is real to him. "Vietnam, Laos, Thailand, etc. —armed, Communist military aggression must be stopped somewhere." Tom feels the best place to stop such aggression is in Vietnam.

Virginia is nineteen and a beautiful girl. She would not go to college. Instead she enrolled in a second-rate drama school in New York. She has serious intentions about becoming an actress—a movie actress, a Broadway actress, an off-Broadway actress, or a Greenwich-Village off-off-Broadway actress. What can a parent do? Telling her that 80 per cent of her classmates are being prepared for work they will never be able to do (the market is glutted with would-be actors and actresses) and that they will wind up as store clerks, nude models, or belly dancers, is like talking into space.

Jim is seventeen, a high-school Senior and captain of the Benjamin Franklin football team. His grades are poor, and he is throwing away his academic ability for athletics. Failed one

24

course last year, and made low *C*'s in the others. But what is worse, Jim has a chip on his shoulder about Negro people. Blacks have entered the high school since he was a freshman. Jim says, "I don't have anything against them—I just don't want to go to school with them." He is the leader of a white gang that is determined to keep Negro students in their place. "Why, Dad," he says, "if we don't do something now, the blacks will take over Benjamin Franklin High." Jim no longer goes to church—he quit Sunday School when he was eleven. He has made friends with several boys whose fathers are leaders in the local John Birch Society. For the past two years the society has been trying to get me out of Briar Wood. They have now infiltrated my church. As yet, I don't know who their leader in the church is, but I will find out. Jim's association with this outfit has not made my lot any easier.

Gail is the youngest, she is fifteen—just ten when you left. You remember her? Everybody remembers Gail! Big blue eyes, blond hair, affectionate and responsive. She was a living doll and in many ways still is. But Sean, Gail is a weekend hippie or yippie or some damn thing that I don't understand. Every weekend she sneaks off to the East Village, dons weird clothes, lugs a guitar around and gets as dirty as possible. Several months ago, some gawking tourists, members of my church, saw her there in yippie uniform and posthaste informed me and a number of people in the church of Gail's transgressions. As you know, I've tried to be sympathetic with today's young people, but when it happens in your own family it's a different matter.

So, my good friend, if these be the joys of family life, you can have them. I'm ready to exchange places with you any day. There are times (today is one of them) when I would give almost anything to be somewhere in sunny California in a retreat center getting three meals a day, all expenses paid, away from the radio and television, able to read and write, away from a critical mother-in-law and a wife who is in the change of life and four kids who are giving me grey hairs, not

to mention a job that is driving me nuts.
Let's trade!

Tom

P.S. Since writing this letter, I've glanced at this week's issue of *Time*. Bishop Shannon has not only resigned as Bishop but has married and presumably left the Church. What a tragedy that the Church should lose one of its most respected men over such issues as birth control and celibacy!

God Is Substance, But Is He Not More Than Custard?

Dear Tom,

Some time ago you mentioned the death-of-God movement and how you had been influenced by it. I have been thinking about what you said, and now in a more leisurely fashion I want to elaborate on the comments I have thus far made. First, it is my considered opinion that this obsession is a theological fad, of a type which is an especial affliction of Protestantism. Within a short time, to hold such a view will not be considered fashionable even among theological intellectuals. Thus, it will be discarded and some new and cunning approach will be advanced. Embracing a succession of ideas about God, Christ, the Church, morality, etc.—some of which are in conflict and opposed to each other—is at once Protestantism's strength and weakness. Strength, because the search for truth is never-ending; weakness because untruth is sometimes fanatically embraced and propagated, and this results in the confusion and/or destruction of both the herald and the respondent. Protestant churches need stability and less addiction to change in faith and practice. The

26

Catholic Church (God help us) needs openness and a willingness to change, where faith and witness will be strengthened rather than weakened.

The second point is that theologians who represent this point of view do not agree among themselves what the "death of God" means. Some write as if they meant the death of a certain kind of God. If so, I am in agreement with them: the big cop, the courtroom judge, the watchful computer, the impersonal God of nothingness. However, as you well know, these ideas have nothing to do with the biblical conception of God, set forth by the Faith as God of Creation, God of the Church, God of our salvation.

Other death-of-God theologians write as if they mean that God once existed but no longer exists. Anthropomorphism may at times be necessary to convey or grasp a certain idea of God ("His breath is upon my neck"), but when the assertion is made that "God is dead," meaning that He who once existed exists no longer, we are dealing here with a childish, anthropomorphic concept, namely, that of man's universal and most distinguishable trait: *mortality!*

Still other death-of-God theologians speak in terms similar to the deistic philosophers of the eighteenth century. Someone or Something created the world, but as of this date He or It has withdrawn both power and compassion from the creation. Here we must ask, if God has withdrawn His presence from the world, why has He done so? Is He bored with the world of His creation, disgusted, unconcerned, or is He obsessed with creating other worlds? If any of these answers is correct, we are here not discussing God but the Devil, not good but evil.

A final group of death-of-God theologians, honest and clear, speak boldly not so much about the "death" of God but about His "eternal nonexistence." There has never been any point in time or eternity when anything resembling the Judeo-Christian God existed; nor has He ever existed as Absolute, Ultimate, Ideal, or First Cause. This world has never known either an immanent or a transcendent God, they say, and frightened man will be more grown up when he accepts that fact as true. Man must discover that he exists alone in a hostile environment, and though he cannot win (death will do him in), survival must become his reason and goal for living. This is the ultimate conclusion of the idea of the "eternal nonexistence of God."

Few of these theologians talk about God in terms of Substance, and for this I am grateful. Many Catholic scholars, past and present, can find no better term for God. This view always conjures up in my mind an irreverent thought. "Substance" to me is a big, sweet glob of custard. We need symbols and words to express what we mean by God, but they should convey ideas of Personality, Mind, Love. Does Substance (Custard) have Personality? Is "It" capable of thinking and making decisions, can "It" love?

You said that when you were a child the question "Who is God" never bothered you. You were bothered by the more profound question, "If God created the world, who created God?" I do not pretend to have an answer to this question; however, when I was in seminary an old professor of theology helped me at this point. He said that existence is the chief characteristic of God. It is as natural for Him to exist and to be the ground of all existence as it is for man to breathe. God does not breathe through manlike nostrils, but He does exist, for existence is His nature. This is what I think Tillich means when he talks about the God beyond God. As far as I know, Tillich does not use the impersonal word "Substance" for God, he uses Being (or Existence). "Being" suggests not a sweet bowl of custard but ultimate Personality, Mind, and Love.

Of course, I have been influenced in my thinking about God by St. Augustine and St. Thomas. St. Augustine saw God as the All-in-All, the great Giver of life, the Creator and Savior. Man was the one most needy, the most helpless. It was St. Augustine who said of God, "Give what thou commandest

28

and command what thou wilt."

St. Thomas by resolving the conflict between faith and reason helped me to arrive at a meaningful affirmation of God. He insists that natural reason starts with investigation, experimentation, and logic. These inevitably lead to the conclusion that God exists. Faith, on the other hand, relies on insight, intuition, and revelation, and likewise leads to the inevitable conclusion of God's existence. Both reason and faith take into account the results of the other, but because of the difference of method there is no distortion, each by the other. A car drives better with two headlights than with one. Reason and faith are the headlights in our search for God.

If God is dead, or if He never existed, how explain the universal law of morality? There is no such thing, you say? Cannibals do not respond to right and wrong as does civilized man, but cannibals have their own inbuilt sense of morality. It may be wrong to eat a man on a given day, or the cannibal may insist that the food for the day must be prepared in a certain way to please the gods and chief of the tribe. There is a sacred code of conduct among thieves. It may not be the code of civilized man, but let a thief break it and he will soon realize that he has done wrong! That universal sense of "rightness" or "wrongness" or "oughtness" in man is what puzzles me. Whence did it come, if not from God? (Don't tell me it's the superego—what a travesty on morality that is!)

God or no God! I suppose when we boil it down our relation to God adds up to Kierkegaard's "leap of faith." You leap, and lo, He is there! Your leap is not into emptiness—you leap into the reality, the power, and the love of God. You have always been one to exaggerate (at least a little). I no more believe what you said about going for the death-of-God fad than I believe what you said in your last letter about Grace. I remember Grace as a gracious, charming southern lady, not only hospitable but also a darn good cook. Where did she learn the blarney cooking? I have never tasted better pork pie and soda bread.

You are a man of many moods, and at the moment a kind of despair is upon you. In the meantime I sit here (getting more anxious by the hour) just waiting, not really knowing what tomorrow may bring. But deep in my heart I know my future is in the hands of men of God who will be just.

I was delighted to get the word about the Smoketown Community Center. To survive white racism and black power today is no small achievement. I'll even settle for a next-door Presbyterian chapel!

Sean

SECTION FIVE

Forty-six and a Family to Support

Dear Sean,

Your last letter made not a damn bit of sense to me. It reminded me of a lecture in a first-year course in systematic theology (which I hated). What is the *purpose* of God's existence? Obviously, he doesn't do very much about the suffering and misery in this world. Do we project a faith in God to prevent us from feeling isolated and alone in a hostile world? Or do we need to be soothed and reassured when we face the crises of life, such as financial disaster, sickness, or death. Or do we believe in God because we feel that such faith is related to life *after* death (at the moment this is my least concern) I find none of these reasons strong enough to require from me an affirmation of God's existence.

Along another line, let me tell you the things I have done these past several years to "make the break." I repeat my former statement, that it is commonly thought difficult for a priest to leave the priesthood, but easy for a Protestant pastor to pick up and leave the ministry. I assure you nothing could be farther from the truth. The first thing a prospective employer wants to know when a preacher goes looking for a secular job is why. Whose wife did he lay? Run off with the organist? How much money did he get away with? What *really* happened?

Well, here are some of the things I did. First, I decided to become a writer, perhaps a genuine author. The writer is self-employed and beholden to no one. In haste and fury, I wrote dozens of articles for royalty-paying magazines and promptly received enough rejection slips to plaster the living room. Then I started on a novel, a real, live contemporary novel accurately reflecting the decay of the Church and ministry. It was titled: *The Decline and Fall of the Church.* Subtitle: "A Modern Minister's Battle with the Establishment." Including the agony of a complete rewrite, it took me eighteen months to complete. I was confident that any name publisher would be glad to have it. In fact, at first I thought of putting it out to three or four companies on bids. But I didn't do that. Instead I sent it forth with a covering letter explaining that I had been a minister for twenty years and that disillusionment was forcing me to leave. The novel was the story of my life in the ministry. I was rudely awakened by a quick bounce. The first publisher did not want it, nor did the second or third. But I was not deterred. I had heard of manuscripts being turned down by nine publishers and snapped up by the tenth. I sent the thing out ten times—yes, sixteen times—and finally gave up. I'm no writer. Making a living that way is impossible.

Second, I considered the poverty program. Most of my departed clergy friends have found a refuge in the government war on poverty. At the beginning, the program offered great promise of being an effective way to deal with poverty in this country. But if there is disillusionment with the

31

Church, there is now greater disillusionment with the so-called poverty program. Poorly organized, poorly staffed, poorly directed, it has been the victim of every conceivable type of bad bureaucracy and mismanagement. Rejects from other positions, many of them clergy, have been given high-paying positions, but the poor are still waiting for the program to touch them. Al Barrington—you remember, pastor of the Morning Heights Baptist Church in Glenview—took an executive position with them and was completely fed up within two years. He has resigned, and I don't know what he is doing now. So I backed off.

Third, I considered selling insurance, and went for a *private* appointment with a large firm in Philadelphia. The manager I talked to was a strong Methodist layman. He was astounded, shocked, and disappointed when I told him my background. What is the Church coming to? Where is the old-fashioned minister who received "the call"? How could I consider leaving the ministry, God's work on earth? Then he told me a long story about his younger years when he almost went into the ministry. He sat back in his plush air-conditioned office, puffed on his cigar, thought about his $50,000 a year job, and piously said, "There's not a day goes by that I don't regret not going into the ministry." After a pause he said, "Besides, you're forty-six years old, with a wife and four kids. This is no time to start a new career." That was that.

Fourth, I decided to teach. It was a shock to learn that my four years of college and three years of theological work did not qualify me to teach in a first-rate high school. I would need a year or so to get "certified." Allen McCall told me to try Beacon Heights Junior College at Boylesville. This is a small Methodist school with a low-grade student body and in serious financial difficulty. I was interviewed and offered the position of instructor in Bible. (I have since learned that no one else would take the job.) I accepted, and next September that's where I'll be. Like Julian's wife, Grace will have to go to work. The salary will be about half what I make now.

Speaking of Allen, I received a letter from him today. He enclosed several promotional clippings, hinting that if I had used such methods I would not now be so dissatisfied with the ministry. The first, from a noted "promotional" church leader and directed to pastors, read "Did you ever feel the thrill of a pastor's experience when his church is moving ahead, packed at every meeting and a nice crowd out at the midweek service?" Allen says that this and more has happened to him since he has been at his big "mainline" church.

Then he confessed that his success in the ministry was due to following the suggestions of Dr. George W. Crane, who writes a column called "The Worry Clinic." He enclosed the following Crane formula for pastors who really want to achieve success in the ministry.

> Remember names and faces. It inflates the ego of parishioners to have their priest or clergyman call them by name.... Name at least three parishioners in your sermon every Sunday, in an incidental but complimentary manner. Urge classes to divide into teams with a captain over each. Schedule short contests every month, with the winning team to be entertained at a picnic or wiener roast by the losers ... praise those who arrange the altar flowers, as well as the ushers, singers, and especially the cooks for the church suppers.

Allen has mastered the art of manipulating people, of turning persons into objects. He is the only man I know who consistently does right and good things for the wrong reasons. So long as evangelism was popular, he milked it for all it was worth. Then he tried peace of mind, and opened a clinic in his church. He rode this for a number of years until it began to peter out. Since then he has gone for coffee houses, jazz masses, rock-and-roll hymn-sings, interpretative dances, touch-ins, feel-ins, forty-eight-hour seminars in spiritual living (men and women shacked up for a weekend

33

in some kind of a Zen meditation excercise) small, intimate study groups, live-wire prayer groups—you name it, he's done it!

While I'm on the subject, and since our correspondence on more than one occasion has taken a confessional twist, I'll mention one more item. As you know from our earlier soul-deep conversations, I have never been interested in any woman except Grace. Some preachers (and priests, I presume) have continuous "female troubles," and others have off-and-on clandestine experiences. As I have listened to several of our clerical friends tell graphic stories of how young women, old women, widows, and divorcees make a play for them, I have felt left out. To my knowledge no woman has ever made any hint of a proposition to me! But I must make this confession. There is one woman in all the world who could bowl me over—I think I could go to bed with her. That woman is Jo McCall. You've met her many times. What a face, what a figure, what hair and eyes—and an attractive, engaging personality! She builds me up whenever we're at a party or a meeting. She puts her hand gently on my arm and in a sweet, low voice says, "Tom, you're the greatest." What the hell does she mean by this? It drives me up the proverbial wall.

It's a practice of mine never to give a hundred points to any woman. If she has a nice figure, she'll have an unattractive face. If she has both a nice figure and face, she'll have a miserable personality. If she has a nice figure, nice face, and pleasing personality, I assure myself that such a woman is sexually frigid. Allen and I were in a bull session several months ago, and he cleared up this last point for me. "Jo," he said, "is always ready ... and can't get enough."

I forced a smile but inwardly groaned. That's all on this subject, or you'll get the idea that I'm jealous of him.

Grace's mother moved in with us last week, and things are pretty bad. Father died a year ago and the old lady has been at loose ends, living at various times with her several children.

34

She scolds Gail from morning to night—there's no discipline in our family. She will supply it.

Let me hear from you soon.

Tom

P.S. I failed to mention that while I was looking for a job I considered selling stocks and bonds, automobiles (used cars), and operating a filling station. Somehow, I couldn't get the right connection for any of them.

It Could Be the Garden of Eden

Dear Tom,

It was something of a revelation to hear you describe the difficulties the Protestant minister has in breaking out. I always assumed it was relatively easy—the lack of stigma, community acceptance, nondiscrimination by employers, etc. Of course, I've been close to the problem of the separated priest, and I can assure you there is no agony like that which he endures. This is created by public suspicion, community rejection, the inability to find employment, the hostility of his own church, and most of all, the anger and embarrassment of his own family.

I told you that Marie and I had thought through the various implications of leaving the Church and getting married. Our problem would have been perhaps less complicated, yet it would have had many difficult spots. Marie's parents have money, but she also has an independent trust fund, set up by an adoring aunt who died when Marie was fifteen. We could have lived comfortably on her income even if I didn't find immediate work. For several months I scouted the possibili-

35

ties. Since my major academic interest has been in Latin American studies as well as the Spanish language, I naïvely thought it would be relatively easy to get a job teaching on either the high-school or the college level. However, once a prospective employer learns that he is dealing with an ex-priest, the cool reaction is instantaneous. So—believe it or not —I planned to take a full year to complete research and write a biography (not a novel!) on the life of Che Guevara. Immediately after the Castro revolution I went to Cuba with a small committee of priests from our diocese to ascertain what the effects of the revolution might have on the work of the Church. Incidentally, I found that most of the priests in Cuba were imports from Ireland and Spain. They were in conflict with Castro, who subsequently deported them all. Other priests were treated not too harshly and to this day the Church is able to function in Communist Cuba. While there I met Che Guevara, and he impressed me more than anyone else. Highly educated, articulate, and impassioned, he appeared to have a genuine commitment to eradication of the brutalizing poverty that flourished under Battista. I was shaken by the apparent indifference of the Church to widespread poverty in Cuba, and embarrassed by the commitment of men such as Che Guevara. Well, anyway, I didn't leave the Church, I didn't get married—and I didn't write the book. Perhaps someday I will. Che is dead, but his spirit lives on.

What do I want to do when I get out of Santa Bella, you ask. My first choice is to return to Puerto Rico and work in the villages and the farming country with people who need help. However, I'm not likely to be reassigned to Puerto Rico. So, I'll take a parish anywhere.

Puerto Rico could be the Garden of Eden, and I strongly recommend it to you for a visit. It's too bad that people in the States know so little about this fabulous island and its people. The principal problem of Puerto Rico is not race but class. Fifty per cent of the people merely subsist—they do have the bare necessities of life; 40 per cent live in poverty, which means poor housing, poor medical care, poor education. Ten per cent comprise the "aristocracy"—wealth, old and new. The upper class with its political and economical connections in the States is getting more affluent, while the 40 per cent of desperately poor are worse off than they have ever been. The standard of living for those in the middle bracket—those who subsist—has risen somewhat in the past ten years. But still their needs are great.

In spite of the limited means of most of the people, they appear happy. This is labeled by some as being "lazy" and "unambitious." Perhaps they are, but it is also possible that they have discovered certain joys in life greater than those of work or possessions. People in the villages and small towns sing, dance, drink, make love, and sleep. There is a refreshing spontaneity about their parties and festivals.

The climate is even better than in California. With warm sunshine and trade winds the year round, the weather is a blend of a New England spring and summer. Temperature averages about 75° November–April, 80° during May–October. In the mountains—my favorite area—it's much cooler. Rainfall varies from about 30 inches in the Lajas Valley to well over 100 on Mt. Yunque in the National Forest. The humidity is also not so great as in our southern states.

There is an amazing variety of plant life. Palm trees grow along the seacoast, bamboo along the interior roads and streams. Tulip trees, hibiscus, and poinsettias are abundant—you don't plant them, they just grow! In the areas of great rainfall there is a jungle of tropical and subtropical trees and plants—giant ferns, orchids, and hanging vines. Flowers, of course, bloom the year round. It is a natural, undeveloped, unmarred paradise. Where do I want to be reassigned? The mass of people on that lovely island need help, and I wish it were possible to return.

I must tell you about my first visit to the psychiatrist. Every-one here at Santa Bella is extremely polite. Those of us who have been sent here for one reason or another are "guests."

37

We are not confined by force to the grounds, we are simply "requested" not to leave. Each week we are interviewed by one or two people on the staff—an older priest, a younger priest, a pastor, an educator, a physician, and of course a psychiatrist. Yesterday morning I saw the psychiatrist. He is a Jesuit, a man about my own age. When I entered the office, he greeted me warmly with a smile and a handshake and then offered me a cigar, then a cigarette. (I sat in a chair, not on a couch.)

We parrried with small talk for several minutes. He was sizing me up, but I had the feeling that a considerable amount of information about me had been in his hands for some time. "How long have you been in the States?" "How did you like Puerto Rico?" "Where was your home originally?" The latter question was his way of asking about my family. I told him in some detail about my boyhood in Ireland, my mother and father, my two sisters. He asked me to describe my feelings for my mother and father. "Easy," I said, "—respect and love." He pressed me further: "Was I obedient to my parents as a young child?" I answered, "More obedient than disobedient. I could never bring myself to hurt them."

Then he said, "Tell me about your younger brother." I gave him Tim's age and the fact that he operates a private school in Hong Kong. I was reluctant to divulge any more information on this subject. But the doctor persisted, "Did he attend Catholic or secular schools when he left Ireland?" "Secular," I answered. "He married a girl of no religious faith or church affiliation."

After this he leaned back, put his feet on his desk, blew a smoke ring, and said, "Father O'Malley, you've been a priest for fifteen years and you're still having a difficult time adjusting to the life of the Church. I'd like to hear your interpretation of why this is so."

I was surprised. It was the direct, frontal approach rather than indirection. I told him that I love the Church and everything about it. The prohibition against saying Mass is almost more than I can bear. I believe in God, I believe in Jesus, the Son of God who lived, was crucified, buried, and resurrected. I believe in the Holy Ghost, who is one with the Father and the Son, and who is with us in our waking and sleeping hours to defend, protect, heal, and strengthen us. I believe in the blessed Virgin Mary, the Mother of Our Lord, and I accept without question the validity of the seven Sacraments.

"Father O'Malley," he said, "you're one of the new breed of priests in the Church, radical and undisciplined—" At this point I interrupted him and said coldly, "I do not consider myself either radical or undisciplined. I'm a traditionalist trying to preserve the truth and beauty of the Church, and I consider it my duty to oppose those within and outside of the Church who seek to mutilate both its original teachings and its spirit."

Once more he was on the offensive. "You took the vows of chastity, poverty, and obedience. Your ministry has been one of flagrant disobedience to your superiors." Then he described in detail the episode in Briar Wood, culminating when I went on television and called my Bishop a racist. In Puerto Rico I publically disobeyed Bishop James McManus. Against his specific instruction, I urged Catholic citizens to vote for Governor Münoz, the man who set up birth control clinics all over the island. I embarrassed the Church, including the Holy Father, with remarks at the University of Puerto Rico (where I defended the position that the United States should recognize the government of Cuba). His voice grew hard as steel as he said, "Your recent political actions are closer to those of Fidel Castro than to the Holy Father's. Is this not so, Father O'Malley?"

I told him that to my knowledge I had not violated any basic concept of canon law, or any teaching of the Church, or any intent of the spirit involving the Faith. I have on certain limited occasions disagreed with my superiors, when

39

I felt they had turned from the Faith of our fathers. I did this on the basis of "conscience," which ancient canon law has always placed above dogma. I cited as an example my opposition to my own Bishop on the subject of racism through the ages. The Roman Catholic Church has an excellent record of insisting on the ministry of the Church to all people, regardless of race. Both in our schools and at the altar, the position of the Church has been the position of Our Lord. Only in the United States and South Africa has the heresy of "supremacy" and separation become a part of the life of the Church. My Bishop by his life, his teachings, and his actions was promulgating a heretical doctrine. My conscience demanded that I oppose him. Then I reminded the psychiatrist that my position is identical with that of a large number of Catholic theologians in this country as well as such men as Father Edward Schillebeeckx of Holland. (When I mentioned the latter, the good doctor flung his hands in the air in disgust.)

But I stunned him when I repeated a memorized quotation from an article by Father John A. O'Brien of Notre Dame. (The psychiatrist is a graduate of Notre Dame!) Father O'-Brien said, and these are his precise words, "An enlightened conscience is the immediate and supreme arbiter of a person's moral decisions. This means that the conscience is the supreme court, whose verdict is final and binding upon him. One may not only follow it, but he *must* follow it."

The doctor was silent for a long time. Then he slowly said, "You're in worse trouble than I originally thought."

I stood and requested permission to ask him a question. He nodded. "Father, I am sure you've seen certain corruptions within the life of the Church which were encouraged and perpetuated by immediate and distant superiors. Have you never once rebelled against them or sought to challenge them?"

With a gesture of impatience, he waved his hand. The interview was over.

40

I had a letter today from Tim. He is encouraging me to leave the Church and come to Hong Kong to teach in his school. The school of which he is headmaster is unique. It is academically superior and very expensive. Good education in the Orient, as elsewhere, is hard to come by. There is a singular requirement for the admission of a student. Wealthy parents—and there are numbers of them in Hong Kong, not only from England and the States but from many countries— whose child is admitted, must also pay the *full* tuition, room, and board of a child from a disadvantaged home (and of these the number is without end). It would be a thrill to be with Tim. I have always loved and admired him. However, with the priesthood, I shall remain! "No man putting his hand to the plow and looking back is fit for the Kingdom of God."

Sean

SECTION SIX

Play It Again, Tom

Dear Sean,
    I'm with Tim!
    Get out while you're still young. The offer to teach in Hong Kong sounds exciting.
    Christmas is upon us, and I find preaching my twelfth Christmas sermon to the same congregation quite a burden. I have told them about Herod and the Wise Men, the angels and the shepherds. I haven't got around to the Virgin Birth, by which you appear to place such store. The irony of these

41

times is that if you preach the core of the Christmas message, "Peace on earth, good will to men," you are labeled a "peacenik" or "pinko" or a "Communist dupe." God knows what we would be called if we preached on the text, "Blessed are the peacemakers"!

Want to know how our Protestant men feel about the ministry? I had lunch with Joe Farthing, pastor of Briar Wood Baptist Church, and he gave me a clipping from *The Crusader*, the widely distributed paper of the American Baptist Convention. It was an anonymous letter from a parish minister. It was titled "Really Fed Up." The text reads:

Really Fed Up

I am fed up with complimentary comments at the door but little indication that the message has been received.

I am fed up with being expected to fit into traditional patterns which are contrary to my convictions.

I am fed up with being careful not to "hurt feelings" even though those of myself and my family are rarely considered.

I am fed up with drafty parsonages, inadequate salaries, and car allowances that are less than one-fourth of the required expense.

I am fed up with fund-raising activities, with Santa Claus in the church and with 101 other activities that belong anywhere but in the church.

I am fed up with people who gloat about the large bank accounts they have for their children's education while I must go on year after year knowing that if my child goes to college, he'll have to do it on his own.

In short, I'm fed up. I'm fed up enough that—even though I have been a pastor for several years and even though I'm approaching middle age—I am seriously considering going into a secular profession. And before I am labeled by the reader as one who is leaving the plow, may I remind him that ministers aren't the only ones who are expected to "plow."

And this is the attitude of a growing number of ministers. I have seen too many good men called to churches, with an immediate attempt begun to see how much he can "take" before he breaks down.

Statistics indicate that in 1970 there will be a shortage of 50,000 ministers in the United States. Unless something changes before very long, there will be 49,999 others and myself.

I *am* fed up!

(Name withheld for obvious reasons)

By the way I called Julian several weeks ago to tell him you were in the States. I could not get by his two secretaries, and he did not return my call. I wrote him a letter the next day, but as yet I have had no reply. Of course, Julian was not much of a letter writer and his responsibilities with the paper have multiplied the last couple of years.

Julian's two reasons for departing from the ranks of the clergy, irrelevance and loss of freedom, hit me pretty hard this week. I attended a joint meeting of our elders and deacons and came away more discouraged than ever. Not simply because of a routine meeting of the leaders of the Lawrence A. Vandergrift, Sr. Presbyterian Church, but *because this is a miniature of today's Church.* The deacons took their share of the evening deploring the poor job the ushers have lately been doing. The cornice of the roof has been leaking. The decision had to be made whether to replace the cornice or the entire roof, which is showing its age. The baptismal font was pushed over by certain young people known as "vandals." I later learned that this travesty was accomplished by two kids, seven and eight years old, playing hide-and-seek.

The elders had more weighty problems. First, visiting shut-ins in recent months has been negligible. Though elders should do a certain amount of this type of visiting, it was hinted that the pastor had not been doing his share. Second, a teen-age combo group wanted to use the basement of the parish house for rehearsals—on a *Sunday* afternoon. The elders refused permission to use church property in such a way on Sunday or *any* day of the week. What the world needs now

43

is more "spirituality," not less. The third and final point on the agenda concerned a petition being circulated by certain people in the neighborhood calling for permission to erect a tavern on the corner of our block. Here the blood pressure of those present rose. To a man they voted to fight the petition with all their strength, even if it meant sending a special committee to City Hall. A counterpetition was drawn up, and there were men who volunteered to work day and night circulating it. One of them was Hank Bowers. Remember Hank? He owns the Dependable Garage on Main Street. Started out, he says, as a one-pump filling station operator. Hank personally wanted to circulate the antitavern petition. I have also learned that he is the contact member in my congregation with the local chapter of the John Birch Society. He and several other men in the church are determined to get me not only out of the pulpit but out of Briar Wood. It almost makes me want to stay! But come September I'll be teaching in a "safe" little Methodist junior college!

I attend meeting after meeting such as the one I have described. I know there are times when I exaggerate, but believe me this is accurate reporting. In such meetings you would never know that this nation is being torn apart by the race question—white supremacy and black power. You would never know that slums are growing faster in the U.S. than decent housing, that children in various parts of the country are literally starving to death. And you certainly would get no impression that Vietnam even exists. It is the one topic most surely avoided. Our laymen must come to grips with a broken baptismal font and a tavern on the corner!

Sean, do you remember a young man by the name of Dan Brewster? He is the mayor's son and had been in law practice in Briar Wood only a short time before you left. He's a gradu-

ate of Yale College and Yale Law School, an extremely bright
fellow. Dan and a young physician, John Breaker, came to see
me yesterday. It was an unusual conference and left me more
then puzzled. Dan is certainly unlike any lawyer I ever had
in any of my churches. He is a crusading liberal, dislikes the
American Bar Association and has a strong sense of the mission of the Church.

Breaker is a little older but still under forty. He cannot
abide the AMA for the same reason that Dan refuses membership in the Bar. He, too, is a social activist! I asked them
if they were alone in sharing this point of view or whether
they represented an appreciable percentage of young
professional men. They laughed and said I was revealing the
generation gap simply by asking. They assured me they were
not alone—that a high percentage of young business and
professional men had rejected the success values of their
elders and are determined not simply to correct glaring
abuses within their own professions, but to meet head on the
major social problems of the community and the nation.

Where have I been? To me, lawyers and physicians represent the most rigidly conservative groups in American society—self-centered, greedy, and worshipers of the profit
motive. Yet here were two dynamic young fellows, highly
educated and highly trained, thinking less about personal
security, country clubs, and cars than they were about the ills
of the nation.

What did they want of me? "We have organized a new
church in Bay Ridge and we want you to help us, to be our
leader." They further explained that they do not have a
church building and never intend to erect one. They rent a
ten-room house where necessary work of the church is carried on. They have been organized a little over a year and
have fifty-two members, all young married couples. Fifty-two
as opposed to my fifteen hundred! They apparently are without the hang-ups of conventional church people. Members of

45

the Bay Ridge church are unanimously opposed to the Vietnam war, and to register their opposition they have staged marches and protests. They are crusaders for the acceptance of people regardless of race or color in all walks of life. They have strong feelings about poverty. Though they believe poverty is a federal problem, it must be dealt with on the local level by the church and the city government. Thus the "business meetings" of their congregation are not concerned so much with repairing the roof or the tavern on the corner as with the issues of war and peace, race, poverty, education, child care, housing, medical services, and so on.

They asked me to "come over and help them." Sean, I felt guilty as a bird-eating dog. I hemmed and hawed and finally told them I would give their proposition some consideration. Let's face it. Their church is a small community church without standing or influence in the city, and will probably remain so. Salary would be negligible—I have two more children to put through college. However, they seemed pleased when I told them I would consider their invitation. It is encouraging to know that all laymen are not exactly like those with whom I struggle each week.

Tom

P.S. Your quote from Father O'Brien is a shocker. The Catholic's "enlightened conscience is the supreme court"—I hope you have this documented. I always thought the Pope was the supreme court in *all* matters pertaining to faith and morals, and that all good Catholics, including priests, automatically accepted that. If the Pope is to be challenged at the point of his infallibility, I wonder what this means for the future of the Roman Catholic Church.

To Our Parents We Are Children

Dear Tom,

I was at first amused, then saddened by the "Really Fed Up" clipping you sent. It is funny because of its satirical manner, but sad because of the bitterness of the minister. Why is he so bitter? Of course the church he serves has its faults, but could something be wrong inside his own spirit? Is he frustrated because his church is smaller in membership than those of his classmates? Has he not received the recognition due him? Has he had to scrimp on a miserly salary? Is he too long "stuck" in one place of service? Or—and this is a big "or"—is he unhappily married? I have observed that certain Protestant ministers, caught in the agony of an unhappy marriage, project their misery onto their jobs. Their work in the ministry must then take the blame for sour and frustrated feelings.

I received a letter from my parents this morning. They sense that something is wrong. I have spared them the details of the various difficulties I have had with the hierarchy. But now that I have been at Santa Bella so long they are anxious. Am I being punished? Am I considering leaving the priesthood? This last possibility, if true, would indeed be the death of both my mother and father. They are poor Irish sod farmers who have had little of this world's goods. The Church has been their life, they have loved it and depended on it to see them through many disappointments and heartaches. They lost six babies, either in childbirth or before the age of one. My older sisters, who have never married and have remained at home, have been a comfort to them, yet both my father and mother silently regret that neither has ever married. The call of God that came to their older son has been their greatest source of joy and pride. The last time I was home, nine years ago, I said Mass in the village church. My mother wept throughout the service, and as we were leaving the church

47

she embraced me and said, "Now I am ready to die."

Tim has been their cross. Younger than I by three years, he was a lad of imagination and initiative. He came to the States at sixteen and landed in New York a stranger without money, friends, or a home. He earned a high-school diploma going to school at night. He worked his way through City College and was eventually awarded a master's degree at Columbia.

I finished college in Ireland, and by the time I arrived in the States for my seminary training, Tim was well on his way toward success. He has never stopped. The month he graduated from college he married a lovely girl from the Bronx, a classmate—a darling girl, but without any religious training or commitment. Tim had given up the Faith before he met her. They were married at City Hall. He and Nancy now have three children, and Tim proudly says that none of them has ever been baptized. Unfortunately, he communicated the details of his marriage and loss of faith to our parents. It was a blow from which they have never recovered. Their Irish son, a true child of the Church, married outside the Church, not to a Protestant, which to them would have been a tragedy, but to an unbeliever—even worse. Now their grandchildren are being raised as unbaptized heathen destined forever to the fires of hell.

After Tim married, my dear mother went to the priest of the village church, explained the situation to him, and asked if he would hold a funeral service for her erring son. This he refused to do, but he suggested a number of prayers for the dead which she could recite in the privacy of her own soul.

How can I convince them that I myself don't intend to leave the priesthood or the Church? Of course I never told them about Marie and the narrow escape I had there. I've often wondered if my fear of what the news of such an event would have done to them influenced my decision. The subconscious is tricky, who can fathom it? But after that test of agony there is no danger that I'll ever again want to leave.

I remember Hank Bowers, an unpleasant fellow who held an important position with the Legion. I wish he had been less active in certain types of politics and more diligent with his business at the garage. I finally had to give up on the old Dependable and take my business elsewhere.

My regards and good wishes to you and the family for a blessed New Year.

Sean

Sand in Our Shoes

Dear Sean,

In commenting on the "Really Fed Up" clipping you wrote about Protestant ministers projecting the frustrations of an unhappy marriage onto their work. It sounded as if you were trying to tell me something. Actually, my marriage is not all that bad. Grace and I have made it for twenty-two years, and I suppose we have squeezed as much happiness out of the relationship as most couples. True, she is undergoing change of life and has developed semiparanoid traits such as morning-and-night nagging and accusations. True, she is more and more like her mother. True, she is not as eager in bed as she once was (but, my boy, there was a time!). True, she has had difficulty in becoming emancipated from a Georgia Fundamentalist background. She has tried, but the urge for the old gospel hymns, an old-fashioned revival meeting and getting saved are just below the surface.

If I am projecting any of my unhappiness onto my work it

49

is the terrible sense of emptiness and despair I feel about Tom, Jr. His enlisting in the Army, being sent to Vietnam, and his militaristic viewpoint about our involvement in the affairs of that unhappy nation have just about done me in. I felt an estrangement between Tom and myself as early as his first year in high school. But I was powerless to do anything about it. I could not communicate with him; nor he with me. It should not come as a surprise that he wants to destroy Communists. He can legally destroy them, but it is a little embarrassing as well as illegal to destroy his father. He rarely writes. We got a brief note at Christmas, the first in six months. Since the New Year we have heard nothing from him, though we keep writing each week.

Speak of being fed up—as of today I've had it up to my eyeballs. Beyond the trivialities of church work there are four different matters that contribute to my irritation, and I feel like putting them down on paper. First, I am fed up with preachers who are granted honorary doctor of divinity (D.D.) degrees and go around calling themselves Doctor and expecting others to do the same. I worked seven years for my education, and as a result have two lousy bachelor degrees. I could have earned a Ph.D in that time. Why do colleges make themselves silly in the eyes of the intellectual world by giving these degrees to so many clergyman? Could it be that the Reverend has a wealthy member on the board of trustees; or perhaps a member of the Reverend's congregation is in a position to make a significant donation to a particular college? Allen McCall was "doctored" last June by Juniper Women's College, and he will let no one forget it!

Second, I am fed up with memorial churches: Lawrence A. Vandergrift, Sr. Presbyterian Church. Is there anything more nauseating? Are these vain people so frightened by death or the fear that they will soon be forgotten that they must get a church named after them? Some of the names of Roman Catholic churches are pretty gruesome, but with all the blood and tears, I prefer them! The Church of the Precious Savior's

Blood, the Church of the Immaculate Conception, the Church of Perpetual Virginity, the Church of Our Lady of Pompei, the Church of the Holy Agony, the Church of the Most Holy Crucifix, the Church of Our Lady of Sorrows, the Church of Our Lady of The Miraculous Medal. Some of these names strike me as eccentric if not offensive. But compared with the Lawrence A. Vandergrift, Sr. Presbyterian Church, I'll take any one of them.

Third, today I am fed up with denominational bureaucrats. Each one of our major denominations hires, at exorbitant salaries, thousands of these incompetent little men. Except for rolling out more red tape, mailing reams upon reams of mimeographed instructions to pastors—their "key" men— what in the name of God do they do? Someday the grass roots will rise up and scrap all the boards, agencies, and committees, and then the local churches might be free to perform their ministries. Our denomination is getting as bad as the Methodist, and for red tape, multiple reports, special offerings, study courses, etc., that's about as bad as the Church can get.

Fourth, I am fed up with institutions that have lost their nerve. This week President Hiram Waterhouse of Beacon Heights Junior College, and I had a conference—at his personal invitation. I told you that, though no announcement has as yet been made, I had been offered a job as instructor of Bible at that feeble institution. Since he had received some negative reports about my ministry, he had several questions to ask me. Was it true that I organized the Smoketown Community Center and chapel, and is it true that both center and chapel, over the protest of certain outstanding citizens, have integrated—meaning that white boys and girls and black boys and girls play together and pray together? Was it true that I wrote a letter to the *Briar Wood Times* criticizing our effort to preserve freedom in Vietnam? Is it true that I defended certain students involved in the protests at Columbia?

I answered Yes to all these questions. Whereupon the old man said, "Your name was to have been presented to the Board of Trustees at the next meeting. It is just as well that you and I quietly agree to withdraw the recommendation. Frankly, Reverend Jones, our college cannot stand one more troublemaker." So I will not be teaching at Beacon Heights Junior College next September.

Since I am now considering becoming a monk, tell me in your next letter how you spend the days at Santa Bella. Give me the schedule from morning 'til night.

Tom

The Good Life at Santa Bella

Dear Tom,

I always thought I could convert you to Catholicism, but not on the basis of finding an easier, more pleasant existence! Compared with the hectic life of a parish priest, with his three Masses on Sunday, weekday Masses, confessions, etc, the Protestant minister has a good thing going. He just doesn't recognize it.

Concerning my routine at Santa Bella, I must confess it is very little like life in the parish. For one who has always been an activist, I find myself chafing under it. During the four months I have been here, the daily schedule hardly changes. We are up at five o'clock, in chapel by five-thirty for Mass and extended prayers. Breakfast at seven. You would not call it breakfast (I have seen you eat)—cereal and grapefruit. After breakfast until eleven, there is a period for reading, studying, meditation, and private prayers. The books provided must be mastered, especially the ones on obedience. At eleven, there is a private conference with a staff member. Sometimes this is an old man who has been a priest for forty years (he has made it without mishap) or a younger priest strong in the faith (not all younger men are radicals), a physician, or, of course, the psychiatrist.

Lunch is from one to two. As with breakfast, lengthy prayers precede the eating of the meal. During the meal one of the "guests" stands at the lectern and reads in Latin from the Scriptures, a devotional treatise, or the lives of the saints, something carefully chosen. Pope Paul's various pronouncements are read. Little of the brief ministry of Pope John is offered. Unlike the mumbled prayers at mealtime, these documents must be read with great attention to diction and inflection. Of course, all meals are eaten in silence. Though I cannot say Mass, I have thus far had this assignment seven times!

After lunch we are permitted to visit and chat with each other. We stroll through the lovely gardens or sit in the shade of a palm tree. Most of the conversation is general chitchat. Few guests here trust each other sufficiently to speak openly of their problems. However, I have made friends with several men recently admitted, and they have to some extent brought me up to date about such events as riots on the campus, black power, the Vietnam war, and of course the various controversies that are shaking the Church to its foundations.

The evening meal is from seven to eight, with more prayers, more readings, and more silence. After the meal we may use the library until nine, then it is back to the cell for bed. Lights are extinguished by nine-thirty. The bed is a firm board with a light cloth over it, and that's not as bad as it sounds.

The private chats I have with my fellow priests are the highlight of each day. Most of the men are recovering from various stages of alcoholism. Ordinarily they don't stay longer

53

than ninety days. Men with severe sexual problems are confined here, but they constitute a small minority. Occasionally there is a priest who has mishandled parish funds—gambling, trips, parties, etc. But these, too, are in the minority. I am the only one here for disobedience, considered far more serious than any other priestly weakness. My type of difficulty is usually handled by one's senior pastor, or in more serious cases, by the Bishop. For obvious reasons I could not be sent back to Briar Wood or to the Bishop of my diocese. And because of complications it was better that the Bishop of Puerto Rico should not handle my problem. So to Santa Bella I was sent, and here I am being studied, examined, and analyzed, and am hopefully waiting for an appointment with the Father Superior who will make the decision concerning my future.

What do I wear, you ask. No street clothes, no collar. A simple robe, made of sackcloth. Sandals (no socks) are our only shoes. I rather like this type of uniform and wouldn't mind wearing it regularly.

Tom, I would like your interpretations of two prevailing problems in the United States. The men here, my fellow guests, have offered widely differing views on both subjects, and frankly I am somewhat confused. The questions are: First, what is really happening on today's college campuses? Are the protests and riots a conspiracy, or are they in anyway justified? Second, how do you interpret "black power"? Is this reverse segregation, separatism, fascism—or something else?

I know how busy you are, but when you can get around to it, I'd appreciate your views.

Sean

When Work Loses Its Meaning

Dear Sean,

So you think the Protestant ministry is a soft touch? Sometime in the near future I will answer your questions about the revolt of the campus and black power. Today I want to outline for you a day in the life of a pastor. Your existence at the moment is somewhat abnormal, and what I describe in this letter is not to be compared with the quiet tenor of life at Santa Bella, but for blood, sweat, and tears I think my work load will compare with that of most parish priests.

I'll list the day in outline and also offer comments on the daily responsibilities and activities. Since I no longer play golf, yesterday was a typical day. Grace and I got up at 6:30 A.M. and ate breakfast at 7:00 A.M. Jim and Gail were up and dressed by seven-fifteen and ready for the eight-o'clock bus. "Mother" came out of her room just in time to catch Gail in a miniskirt. She raised a ruckus and exploded with, "No sixteen-year-old girl of mine would dress in such a disgraceful manner!"

I closeted myself in the upstairs study and read newspapers, magazines, and journals until eight-thirty and then drove to the church office. I had planned two hours of intensive study for Sunday's sermon. It was necessary to get it in shape on Tuesday because the latter part of the week was crowded: I am to deliver five radio devotionals next week, and up to now haven't the slightest idea what I will say. Perhaps I ought to quit writing you and start tending to shop! You said that this exchange of correspondence has been a life-saver to you. It has meant just as much to me and possibly even more—*it is a catharsis.*

55

When I arrived at church the secretary reminded me that I had agreed to write a brief article for the Sunday bulletin on making church suppers more appealing. They have become a drag for all of us. The bulletin was going to the printer within the hour, so there was nothing to do but sit down and compose a rationale for church suppers. Miss Perkins also reminded me that I was to make three important phone calls, one of which involved a thirty-minute conversation with the chairman of the finance committee. We are beginning our fund-raising campaign, and precampaign plans, including a kick-off supper, have to be made.

At 11:00 A.M. attended a meeting of the program committee of the Ministerial Alliance, of which I am chairman.

12:00 noon. I had lunch with a secretary of the synod (one of the hierarchy). Somehow he had heard that I was leaving the parish, and came to say that he would use his influence to get me a call elsewhere. I assured him that my decision was made and that it was final.

2:00 P.M. Spoke to the monthly meeting of the Women's Auxiliary in the church, after which I taught a special class on "The Mission of the Church."

3:00 P.M. Conducted a funeral service for an elderly man I did not know. The body had been shipped from Arizona. The service was held in Barker's Funeral Home. There were three people present.

4:00 P.M. Conference with a young lady who is planning a June wedding. She wants a big, impressive church wedding. She didn't want to talk about *marriage*, but about "the" wedding. The wedding party would have a matron of honor, a maid of honor, seven bridesmaids, a ring-bearer, a flower girl, plus her father and a host of ushers. There would be two soloists. She was not a member of our church, or of any church, and furthermore she never attends church. She doesn't believe in it. But she wants a big church wedding. I asked her what she felt was the purpose of such a wedding.

56

She replied with considerable honesty, "This is the biggest moment of my life, and for once I'll be front center; I want it done right."

I explained that she must abide by certain rules of the church: (a) She must try to control the florist. At the moment there is a war on between the florists in Briar Wood, and each one tries to outdo the other in decorating for church weddings. (b) No candles in the windows or the aisles; the church candles in the chancel would have to do. (c) She must control the photographer. No pictures during the ceremony. Flash bulbs and a wedding ceremony do not go together. (d) She must be selective in choosing the music. Sentimental songs such as "O Promise Me" and "I Love You Truly" are not acceptable.

At these suggestions the young lady flipped. In the great huff she said that her fiancé was a member of Dr. Allen McCall's church near Philadelphia, and besides, his church would seat more people than mine. Her wedding would be held there. The interview with the prospective bride was terminated.

4:30. Made the rounds of two hospitals (missing St. Elizabeth's, no offense to you). I still never know when to pray and not to pray in a hospital room. A little six-year-old boy had his tonsils removed. The mother, one of our Sunday-school teachers, asked me to have a prayer. After which the little fellow asked, "Am I going to die?"

6:30 P.M. Went to church for a supper meeting of the Fishers of Men Bible Class, where I offered the invocation. Adult classes in our Protestant churches have become little churches within themselves. Sunday-school belongs to laymen, and clergymen would do well to remember it. The choir has often been called the war department, but let a minister make suggestions about changing or discharging teachers, or about the curriculum or the annual picnic, and he will soon discover where the war department is. The theme of many

57

of these adult classes is "Let's play church." No one, especially the minister, must attempt to bring an ounce of reality to them.

8:00 P.M. Attended the preliminary meeting of the Every Member Canvass Committee and the Budget Committee. The canvass will not be launched until next fall, but our leaders feel that during the spring all plans must be made. Nothing can be accomplished during the summer slump. I was particularly interested in getting an increase for the Smoketown Chapel. The Community Center has been taken over by the city and is doing extremely well. Hank Bowers has been opposed to the chapel on the grounds that it encouraged "mixing" of the races. He read a letter from the secretary of the chapel, stating that our gifts and efforts in the past were appreciated but the people who attended the chapel felt they could carry the work alone.

I left the church about ten and was home before 10:30 P.M. Both Jim and Gail were in their rooms, "Mother" had retired. Grace and I had coffee, relaxed until about eleven-thirty and then went to bed.

I said that my work load would compare with that of most priests, and I think this is true. However, there is one difference: you men, for the most part, appear to derive meaning and satisfaction from your work, whereas I (and many of my contemporaries) have lost that meaning. Long hours do not a cynic make, but loss of meaning does.

One other point before I close. I regret that I have never been to Puerto Rico, and am ashamed that I know and care so little about the island and its people. Great masses of Puerto Ricans have moved in and around Briar Wood, including Smoketown. They now compete with Negroes for various types of menial labor. Needless to say their presence has caused a whole new set of class and racial problems. Tell me, if Puerto Rico is the Garden of Eden, why do so many natives leave it?

Tom

The Garden of Eden Needs Tending

Dear Tom,

If Puerto Rico is the Garden of Eden, you want to know why so many people are leaving it. The reason is simple: low wages, high prices, and limited housing, educational, and medical services for workers and farmers. Inflationary economy in the States has had its effect on people here. However, income has not kept pace with rising prices. Thus they are caught in a vicious spiral. San Juan has been converted into a pre-Castro Havana, where hotel prices, are as high as in New York. Prostitutes, call girls, and gambling have become big business. Among the lower classes there is not simply unrest, but despair.

Within the past fifteen years the Commonwealth has made some progress in low-rent housing and medical services, but the surface has hardly been scratched. The government, though it too needs priming, is not as corrupt as that of their neighbors in the Dominican Republic and Haiti.

There are three political parties, each operating from different ideologies. Unlike the States, where little difference appears between Republicans and Democrats, there is considerable difference in the Puerto Rican parties. The Popular Democratic Party has been until recently the strongest political force. Its major strength lies in its close connection with the States. This party is strongly opposed to both statehood and independence. Leaders of the party believe that commonwealth status is far more advantageous. Residents of Puerto Rico are citizens of the United States. The governor is no longer appointed by Washington, but elected by the people. However, the Commonwealth does not have representation in the U.S. Congress, and the people cannot vote in our national elections. Under the present arrangement they do not pay federal income taxes, only a Commonwealth tax. However, citizens of Puerto Rico participate in the U.S. Social Security programs, including Medicare. Young men are subject to the draft and are conscripted according to the laws of the United States. More than 60,000 Puerto Ricans served in the Korean conflict and thousands have been called for the war in Vietnam. (The Vietnam war is as unpopular in Puerto Rico as it is in the States.) The U.S. Supreme Court is the highest court of the Commonwealth, and citizens may now appeal directly to it. The Popular Democratic Party is strong and its position is likely to prevail for some time to come.

The New Progressive Party is in favor of statehood. Leaders of this party insist that the principles which led to the admission of Alaska and Hawaii to the Union apply to Puerto Rico. These people are willing to pay federal income taxes, but they also want the privilege of voting for the President, as well as for Senators and Congressmen. They also feel that Puerto Rico deserves the dignity of being one of the states of the Union. The New Progressive Party is a power to reckon with.

The third political force is the Independent Party, whose primary objective is to gain complete independence from the United States and make Puerto Rico a self-sustaining, autonomous country. This party does not have the strength of the other two. However, it is vocal and militant. Rumor has it that the party's objective is not so much to gain independence from the United States as it is to achieve a direct alliance with the Soviet Union. Though I talked with many people about this, I saw no evidence to support such rumors. These people simply want the freedom to be a self-reliant country. Recent bombings in San Juan have been attributed to members of the Independent Party. I doubt any such connection.

In addition to these three parties there are a number of small splinter groups, most of which are Communistic and therefore underground. Their leaders are not so much concerned about an alliance with the Soviet Union as to set up a government like that of Cuba. Most of them are fanatical

supporters of Fidel Castro. They feel that workers and peas-
ants have little to lose by going Communist and very much
to gain. It is difficult to talk to poverty-stricken people about
freedom when they live with painful scarcity. This is especially true in a city such as San Juan, where there are evi-
dences of extravagance and affluence. Most of these people
are Catholics by faith, some genuinely devout, and not all are
as happy and easygoing as I suggested in an earlier letter. I
was not only a priest to them, but became their friend. Those
with education appear determined to harmonize the basic
views of communism—"From each according to his abilities,
to each according to his needs"—with their religious faith.
Of course, these people have little respect for the upper classes and look for the day when wealth will be distributed
and everybody, including the "fat cows," will have to
work.

Members of these splinter groups, who feel that Puerto
Rico will someday be allied with Castro's Cuba, live with an
illusion. The United States Government would no more per-
mit Puerto Rico to move into the Communist sphere than it
would Texas or Rhode Island. It is my idealistic hope—but a
hope nonetheless—that someday a political system will be
developed under which money and property will be more
equitably distributed, and people will not have to forfeit their
dignity and freedom to share in it.

Several weeks ago, I wrote Julian at the address you gave
me, but I have had no reply. What gives?

Tim wrote again this week. His school needs a teacher in
social studies majoring in Latin America! He is applying the
pressure. Though reared a Catholic, he does not quite per-
ceive the depth of meaning in ordination and the priestly
commitment.

My regards to Grace.

Sean

Julian—the Fall of a Giant

Dear Sean,

Today I am so depressed I can hardly make it. Saw Allen McCall at a ministerial meeting in Philadelphia this week, and he tells me that he is being nominated for Bishop at the next meeting of his annual Conference. The state of the church is even worse than I thought if this can happen! Has there ever been so much emptiness in one man? He has antennae a mile long. They feel their way along until they unerringly reach what people most want to hear. The phonier he gets the more the people love him.

But that chance meeting is not all that has contributed to my low spirits. Grace's mother of late has been giving me a hard time because I am not sufficiently evangelistic. On the living-room table and on my desk in the study she leaves piles of pamphlets: *Are You Saved?, How To Know You Are Saved, Communism in the National Council of Churches, Personal Salvation or Society Salvation?* I complain to Grace but she simply says, "Mother is just trying to resurrect the old-time religion."

Jim is still on his antiblack kick. He has received a football scholarship to the University of Mississippi and will enroll in September. He and his grandmother get along very well.

Virginia is taking her acting courses seriously. She has found something to which she can give herself without reservation and has become less of a rebel. It is pleasant now to have her at home, even though she and her grandmother are constantly quarreling.

Gail is rarely at home on the weekends. She goes the whole bit—the dress, the guitar, rock-and-roll, etc. I don't think she has ever smoked marijuana, but she smokes a pack of cigarettes a day. She says she's been smoking since she was twelve and doesn't intend to quit.

62

Still no word from Tom. The suspense is dreadful. I have thought about going to the Red Cross, but friends assure me that no news is good news. They say that if anything happened to him we would be notified without delay. So we just wait in silence.

I have saved the worst until the last. It concerns Julian Feldman. An elder in my church who has been on my neck for criticizing our involvement in Vietnam brought me several clippings from Julian's paper. They were strong editorials written in a crisp, clear, logical tone. The elder said he had personally checked them out with a relative who works for the paper, and Julian certainly wrote them.

The first one dealt with black power. The conclusion of this editorial was that force had to be met with force. There are 180,000,000 white people in this country, 22,000,000 blacks. White people control the courts, police, and military power. If Negroes are demanding black power and insist on a confrontation, *now* is the time to confront them. If they are asking to be wiped out, then wipe them out.

The second editorial dealt with the campus revolts. (I'll give you *my* views on both black power and campus revolts some other time.) Administrative authorities have abrogated their responsibilities. Protesting students who challenge existing authority should be swiftly dealt with. By this the editorial meant—explicitly—immediate suspension. If the offense is committed a second time there must be expulsion, with no amnesty or chance of readmittance. It further asserted that students should be required to know clearly in advance just what the rules and regulations of a given school are. Admission policy should require from the student an oath to uphold existing practices.

The third editorial dealt with Vietnam. Phony liberals and half-baked intellectuals are responsible for our weakened position in Vietnam. If enthusiastic support instead of insipid criticism had been given the President, this little war could have been wrapped up in six months. The editorial recommends further and deeper involvement, including the possible use of nuclear power, on two counts. First, our country has treaty obligations with many other countries besides Vietnam. If we retreat from the defense of South Vietnam, we break our solemn word, our sacred pledge. Will other countries with whom we have treaties trust us? Second, we must not deceive ourselves: we are not simply defending South Vietnam, a country determined to maintain its freedom—we are defending ourselves, *our* interests, *our* freedom. If South Vietnam goes, so will Cambodia, Laos, Thailand. What then will be the fate of Indonesia and Japan, Australia and the Philippines? If we retreat now, it means we will eventually fight our Asian enemies in California.

I have called Julian several times and written him more than once. You say you wrote him but had no answer. Is there any wonder? I'm sick, that's all I can say—sick.

I must wind up this miserable letter about a miserable week: Monday my choir director—for the last eight years—ran off with a married man twice her age. She left a note, but no one has heard another word from her. Yesterday my assistant pastor and educational director announced his resignation. He is leaving the ministry and taking a job as a salesman for a Wall Street brokerage firm. Members of the John Birch Society have begun to call various members of my church explaining why their pastor is a threat to the community.

This week I contacted a real estate firm in Harristown and have been offered a job selling real estate. I have always liked houses, especially old ones. I told the president of the firm that I would take the position.

If you can write gloomier news than all this, I'll read it and frame it.

Tom

Allen—There's No Success Like Ministerial Success

Dear Tom,

Your remarks about Allen McCall broke me up. Of course he's going to the top—of course people crave to hear what he is saying. As long as he can anoint the guilty conscience with glossy assurances, pious words, and empty prayers, he will be exalted—as we say, "sainted." Is there nothing higher in the Methodist Church than bishop? If there is, his election to that high office is just a steppingstone to personal success, as is every other position he has held.

It is my contention that a Christian must speak and live prophetically. This means saying and doing, not what people want, but what God wants at a given point in history. Jesus was rejected, not because he said, "Consider the lilies of the fields, see how they grow," but because he said, "Woe to you, scribes and Pharisees, hypocrites! for you traverse sea and land to make a single convert and when he becomes converted, you make him twice as much a child of hell as yourselves ... you blind guides straining out a gnat and swallowing a camel ... you have neglected the weightier matters of the law: justice, mercy, faith." Notice that justice comes first in the list.

Julian Feldman is another matter. I remember him when he faced the City of Briar Wood like the lion of Judah, at an open rally in the football stadium, and challenged the politicians who were perpetuating slums, ghettoes, poverty, discrimination, etc. He was truly a giant with a burning sense of justice. I have never met a man who was more sensitive to moral and ethical issues than Julian.

It is still possible that he did not write those editorials. Of course, if he is the editor he would have to acquiesce in them. But there is still some difference between writing them and simply giving permission to another to write and publish. I am trying to hold on to any reasonable hope about him. A

65

magnificent mind, beautiful talent, and courageous spirit such as Julian Feldman's do not cave in so easily.

Most of the priests who entered the retreat at the same time I did have long since left. They have gone back to their parishes or been given special appointments such as working with prisoners, narcotic addicts, or in some cases with college students. I hope to have some word from the Father Superior before long.

Never fear, you will get a new choir director and a new assistant pastor.

I hope you hear from Tom, Jr. before long. The suspense must be agonizing. My prayers tonight will be for Tom, his safety, and his reconciliation with his parents.

Sean

SECTION TEN

Today's College Campus Is a Riot

Dear Sean,

I have at last got around to giving you my version of what's happening on today's campuses. The worst riots have taken place since you were at Santa Bella, so you can't have heard very much about them. It is hard to be objective about the student revolt, but I'll make the effort.

In the first place, a great deal of disorder has been fomented by the criminal element who have infiltrated various campuses. By "criminal" I mean what the word says: living by the code of hoodlums and gangsters. Some of these rioters,

66

extortioners, dope pushers, etc., are bona fide students, some are dropouts, and certain leaders in this category are nonstudents, older men and women who seize upon any opportunity to create chaos, not for strategy to make things better, but for the hell of it. These people, for reasons best known to themselves, hate the government of the United States so much that it is a thrill and a joy for them to produce any kind of disturbance. Their obvious aim is to shut down as many college campuses as possible.

In the second place, certain well-meaning black power advocates have played into the hands of the criminal element. They have done this not simply by rioting, destroying property, and taking over campus buildings, but by making impossible and unrealistic demands on administrators and trustees. One group at a noted university in the East demanded the immediate admission of a thousand black students. All qualifications were to be waived, free tuition, room, and board provided. Students would take no examinations, present no credentials, and they would come from any age bracket! Nor was this all. By their own choice and demand they would live by themselves in segregated dormitories, and the university would provide a separate department in Afro-American studies just for blacks—no whites permitted to take these courses! There is an element of comedy as well as irony in these demands, but the pall of tragedy also hangs over them.

In the third place, there are students morally sensitive to a variety of injustices and outworn policies, who have attempted to register their grievances in a variety of ways. There is no institution in American society, including the Church, that has so desperately needed reform as our colleges and universities. Dr. Martin Meyerson, president of the State University at Buffalo, New York recently said, "I think the American university, in many ways, has changed less than almost any of our American institutions. The most major reformation is called for." This statement from one of the nation's foremost educators is true, but it is paradoxical to the point of farce, for no institution has preached liberalism and tolerance quite so much as our colleges and universities! These places of higher learning have demonstrated a remarkable resistance to change.

The most amazing statement indicting them comes from Robert H. Finch, Secretary of Health, Education and Welfare. Speaking of today's universities, torn by student disorder, he charged that "these universities have brought much of it on themselves. An overhaul of university structures is long overdue." The Secretary contended that in the quest for more and better research grants universities have neglected their primary objective as teaching institutions. His exact words are: "In attempting to serve many masters—government and industry among them—they have tended to serve none of them well." He said further, "The trouble now plaguing American campuses—violence, disruption, confrontation —is a tragic development in the history of American higher education. However, in many instances, the conflict is solidly based in legitimate grievances."

Responsible students are concerned about the campus's relation to giant industries manufacturing sophisticated tools of warfare. They are opposed to the government's use of laboratories, professors, and classrooms for military purposes, and are concerned about the increasing economic dependence of these schools of higher learning upon the government in exchange for military services. They are resentful of the encroachment of the military on the daily life of campuses: the recruitment of students, the ROTC, and the CIA.

Students are concerned about the favored position of senior professors who never teach, but who go through the motion of writing books, some of which are published, some not. No professional man in American society is so pampered and so "deified" as the full professor with tenure! This includes not only salary and vacations, but also his privilege of being consultant to corporations or to the government for fabulous fees. When the poor college professor is thought of, one should never think of senior professors at major universities —they are doing well for themselves!

Students are concerned with the restrictive quota systems whereby minority groups are kept to a minimum or eliminated altogether. They are weary of "liberal" administrations which can show not one Negro on their faculties! They are incensed when a competent professor is dismissed for his antiwar statements and activities ("incompetence" is usually the false charge). Students also rebel against junior-high-school rules and regulations as to hours and rooms, by which colleges and universities attempt to be something they can never be: parents in absentia.

A tragic aspect of the student revolt is that with a more conservative political administration in power, police and military force are likely to be used to stifle not only professional rabble-rousers, criminal elements, and misguided blacks, but also the legitimate efforts of responsible students. Certain limited changes and reforms have already been adopted because of these protests. Let us hope that sheer brute force will not put an end to them.

When do you get out?

Tom

P.S. Students who are protesting apparently have a strong ally in Brig. Gen. Hugh B. Hester (Ret.). General Hester writes in the *New York Times* this morning the following word of warning: "Those who would save this country from the disaster of an industrial-military dictatorship, similar to the one which destroyed Hitler's Germany, have no choice except to unite behind a massive peace movement. This movement should be kept nonviolent, but it cannot and will not be unless the establishment also remains nonviolent.

"The enemy is inside, not outside, our gates. And the President should so inform the people instead of trying to revive old and greatly overworked bogies."

The Verdict Won't Be Long Now

Dear Tom,

Your analysis of the current campus revolt was extremely helpful. Of course, from Puerto Rico I followed the Berkeley and Columbia crises, but as I told you, I have had to depend upon my fellow guests to keep me informed about the events of the past year. Some of the men have been bitter and impatient with the students, believing that they have no worthy objectives in mind. Others are of the opinion that the revolt is long overdue, and that demonstrations and even riots ought to take place on many of our silent Catholic campuses. One of my new friends, a priest from an Eastern faculty, was summarily expelled for insubordination. His field is philosophy. From his description, academic freedom is a myth. The college is run so autocratically that administration, students, and faculty live in fear from one year to the next, not knowing when the ax will fall. Catholic colleges are organized to interpret and perpetuate Catholic truth, the supposition being that "Catholic" truth is equivalent to *the* Truth. He who deviates from what history has handed down is in danger of the wrath of God, as well as dismissal from the ranks. Catholic higher education in the United States has always been inferior. Is it any wonder? I have often pondered the question whether or not you can have a real college if academic freedom is not the life and spirit of the institution. When truth becomes Baptist truth, Methodist truth, Presbyterian truth, or Catholic truth, the pursuit of knowledge becomes a myth.

I received official word from a staff member this morning: the Father Superior leaves for Rome today and will be gone for three weeks. The day after his return, I am to see him. What a blessed day it will be for me! During these long months I have been restless and have resented being confined here, but I must admit that the treatment has been good for me. I have had time to pray and meditate, time to reappraise my own position and the work I have been called to do. Perhaps the world would be better off if everyone, sometime during his lifetime, had a Santa Bella.

The most difficult penalty has been the restriction on saying Mass and taking the Holy Eucharist. I attend Mass every morning, but I just sit and watch. To one who has experienced life and strength from the body and blood of Christ, this denial is most difficult to bear.

You have given me a genuine insight into the campus situation. What about "black power"? You and I have given the strength of our lives to help people understand that color does not matter, that little children of the next generation must work, live, and walk hand in hand. From your point of view, are the advocates of black power opposed to this? If so, do we have on our hands a new form of segregation and separatism? Must blacks imitate the worst in us in order to be men?

Sean

SECTION ELEVEN

Black Power as an Interim Ethic

Dear Sean,

I'm in a writing mood today. Next Sunday is Easter. If Christmas sermons are difficult for me, Easter is impossible. What does one preach about? Immortality to people who want to live it up now and care nothing about a life beyond

71

this life? Communication with the dead? Relationships one to another in the afterworld? The resurrection of Lazarus, dead and in the tomb for four days, body in a state of decomposition, makes the story of the resurrection of Jesus somewhat anticlimactic. Lazarus was raised to new life in this world where he could once again enjoy a glass of wine, a leg of lamb, and a woman in bed. That kind of a resurrection I could preach!

In order to find one more way of putting off writing next Sunday's sermon, I will today give you my interpretation of "black power."

Black power is not one but many movements. First are the Black Muslims, whose leader is the venerable Elijah Muhammad of Chicago. This is the most fanatical and perhaps the most dangerous group among us. Not because these people believe in violence, but because they have a charismatic leader, are well organized, with unlimited sums of money at their disposal, and above all have a well-defined faith to which their followers are unreservedly committed. Black Muslims envision on these shores a separate black nation with a specific territory and their own public officials, including an army and navy. *Total separation* based upon the Nazi concept of racial superiority is the chief motivating force. No delay is too long, no sacrifice too costly—the great day of the Black State is coming!

Second, the Black Panthers. They are committed to the beliefs of the Black Muslims, with one difference. Marxist oriented, they hold to no religious or ethical principles and believe that violence is the way their objectives can be reached. The white man acquired and retains his possessions and his power essentially by violence. Blacks must do the same. Thus bombing, burning, looting, and shooting are justified. Confusion and chaos must be produced in white power structures from one end of the country to the other. Some of their members are on our campuses, but most of them operate in the large metropolitan areas. For the most part they are not from the uneducated, lower classes, but from the higher ranks of black society. Detecting the perpetrators of violence is difficult not only because it is committed under the cover of night and in great secrecy, but because authorities rarely look for such people in middle-class intellectual society. Since the departure of Eldridge Cleaver, this group has no charismatic leader, and their funds are limited.

Third, the movement of Martin Luther King. It is felt by many that at the time of his tragic death King was losing influence with his people. I don't buy this. At the time of the assassination, he was the most powerful leader of black people in this country. His vision of equality, freedom, and justice had permeated millions of minds, and his way of nonviolence, instead of being discredited, was the most powerful force in the land. Why do I say he was the most powerful black leader? Is it because he was a magnificent writer and speaker? Surely his "I have a dream" speech in Washington and his "Letter from a Birmingham Jail" will live forever. No, he retained his leadership and influence because, to the very end, he put his life where his words were. Just before the assassination he served a sentence in an Alabama jail. If white people want to know what hell is like, let them try to imagine a black civil rights leader in an Alabama jail. Many black leaders talk loud—"Let's blow hell out of them"—but when the chips are down, they will use any maneuver to stay out of jail, including leaving the country. I once asked Dr. King how many times he had been jailed. "I've forgotten," he said. "Why keep count?"

Martin Luther King repudiated separatism and segregation, he denied the principle of racial superiority, and he abhorred violence. What about his movement today? The leader is gone and the organization he headed is weakened, but let no one believe that the 22,000,000 black people of the United States have forgotten this mighty prophet. My calculated guess is that there are more blacks who subscribe to the basic beliefs of Martin Luther King, including his insistence on nonviolence, than to those of all other organizations and groups combined.

The last group, recently emerged, are Negroes whom I call responsible radical blacks. These people do not accept the principle of racial superiority, neither do they practice offensive violence, but they do believe that, at this stage of the black man's development in the United States, separatism is necessary. They accept this not as an absolute but as an "interim ethic." Black power means *economic* and *political* power. So long as black people are diffused (or integrated) into an overwhelming white society, they can never realize the weight and thrust of their own strength, nor can they know their true identity. Token integration is more deadly than segregation and discrimination. One or two blacks will be put into an all-white dormitory or office. Thus the dormitory or office will be "integrated," but the blacks will be ignored or observed. Whites will be able to see at close range how Negroes comb their hair, shower, and sleep. Blacks can take the snubbing, but they resent the "observation"—as if they were insects in a biology lab, and they especially resent being used by any segment of the establishment. Though I believe it is a mistake, I can understand the press for the segregated life where they can be with "their" kind. But leaders of the movement interpret separatism as an interim ethic. To make it an absolute would be to deal in idolatry. When *political* and *economic* power has at last been achieved on a scale commensurate with their numbers, the black man will be more than willing to make a graceful reentry into the white man's world, for the simple reason that that world will have also become his world.

The other day your successor, Father Giovanni, taught me a lesson about black power and interim ethics. Since you left he has been the most militant leader for civil rights of anyone in Briar Wood. He took to the streets and led the fight that broke the back of the real estate monopoly. Last year an ordinance was finally passed by the City Council regulating the sale and rental of apartments and houses. This meant that a number of Negroes have been able to get out of Smoketown and buy homes in Spring Glen. Father Giovanni paid a price for his militance in behalf of black people. The Bishop is infuriated again and is threatening to suspend him; he has been attacked on the streets by vigilante groups; dozens of white families have ceased attending St. Elizabeth's. He is harassed day and night by threatening phone calls. He is labeled an "extremist," "nigger lover" and "Communist." I don't see how he has withstood the pressure.

Now that the fight for open housing has been won, Negroes are approaching equality of opportunity in Briar Wood. Housing was the hardest nut to crack. But the amazing turn of developments is that Father Giovanni has been fiercely rejected by the black community, especially the leaders. In a variety of ways they have indicated to him (as they have to me) that they want no more of his leadership or friendship! They insist on carrying the ball by themselves. Father Giovanni is "white" or "whitey." Black power advocates—even those of the "interim ethic" persuasion—see in his efforts a move to weaken the religious, political, and economic life of the black community. Black pastors are making every effort to win back to their churches those of their people who have strayed to white churches. Thus they are reestablishing the old ways of segregation.

I asked Father Giovanni how he felt about this, and he laughed and said, "I didn't do it to win their favor—I did it because it was right. Besides, the move by the blacks to segregate will not last forever."

By the way, you have never answered my question: "Why were you shipped out of Puerto Rico, and why are you under suspension?" You said that the controversy over birth control had nothing to do with it. Thus, my curiosity was ignited—

75

if not the race problem or birth control, what then? I realize this may be a sensitive question. If you would rather not answer, skip it. I'll understand.

Tom

The Charge Is Subversion and Disobedience

Dear Tom,

You are correct. It was not the race problem nor yet birth control. And you are correct in thinking that the question of why I left Puerto Rico is sensitive. But though I'm somewhat embarrassed, I'll try to describe the circumstances that led to my expulsion from the Commonwealth and confinement at Santa Bella. I have been here long enough so that I can interpret these events from a more accurate perspective.

Some students at the University of Puerto Rico learned that I was an admirer of Che Guevara, and I immediately became a bit of a hero to them. They invited me to address a forum with the preassigned topic: "The United States Government Should Recognize the Government of Cuba." The opposing speaker was a U.S. Government official. He had been attached to our delegation at Santo Domingo when our troops went to the support of the military junta which overthrew the constitutionally elected government of the Dominican Republic. Before the evening was over, my opponent in debate charged me with "subversion," "disloyalty," and being a paid agent of Castro's government.

I stuck to my original point. The U.S. Government has little to lose and much to gain from recognizing the Cuban Government. I began by using the naval base of Guantánamo as an illustration. The base scares no one, and militarily it has no significance in the Western Hemisphere or anywhere else. We are there because of sentiment and pride rather than security. Our presence on Guantánamo gives Castro his strongest propaganda weapon with his own people and with the struggling countries of Latin America. The people in many of these countries do not trust the government of the United States, especially since we operate through the hated CIA. The base at Guantánamo is Castro's most valuable tool. If we should close it tomorrow and withdraw from Cuban soil, *he,* not our government, would suffer.

We do business with the greatest Communist country of them all—Russia. We not only do business with other Communist countries such as Yugoslavia, but to these governments we make huge loans and gifts. If restrictive policies had been practiced by the United States on any of these countries, sympathy and increased trade both from allies and potential enemies would have resulted.

The U.S. Government probably finds the futile attempts to isolate Cuba distasteful, but it cannot do otherwise because of politics. Interestingly enough, left-wing extremists in the U.S. would resist a change in policy more than right-wing ones, and this for two reasons: first, as with Guantánamo, our present policy of nonrecognition is ready-made propaganda for Cuba. Second, left-wing extremists would oppose recognition because Castro (rather than Russia) has created a true Marxian government. Contacts with the United States would corrupt that government, even as Russian itself has been corrupted by capitalistic ways.

Latin America in recent years has seen the rise of every type of cruel fascist military dictatorship. With many of these countries, now controlled by police-state tactics, the U.S. Government has not seen fit to sever diplomatic relations. On the contrary, we have poured millions upon millions of dollars into the hands of dictators for their personal use, including padding their Swiss bank accounts. The broken, submerged people of Latin America know what this situation

77

is, and they ask, "Among all countries in Latin America why does the United States try to destroy Cuba?"

The newspapers, of course, gave my remarks at the university front-page attention, and again there was havoc to pay with my superiors. But this was only the beginning. At the end of my first year in Puerto Rico, and with the help of several other young priests, I created in La Perla, the slums of San Juan, an organization which came to be known as the "Center for Christian Action." The Church has been slow to deal with basic problems in Puerto Rico, thus the Center became a spring of hope both to the priests who were working with me and to the people. Group discussions were held on three burning issues. First, we must find the most effective way to influence the Puerto Rican government to cope with slums, education, and health facilities. It was our plan to hold peaceful marches and demonstrations similar to those so effectively employed by Martin Luther King. Second, we discussed the necessity of a massive job training program which would supplement what the U.S. Government is doing in Puerto Rico. Workers had to be adequately compensated while they were in training. Third, some way had to be found to deal with the "aristocracy," the 10 per cent who hold so much of the island's wealth. Tax loopholes had to be stopped and a program of land reform initiated. As the United States continues to pour millions of dollars into the Commonwealth, the upper class has grown richer and richer, and there appears to be no end to their private accumulations.

At no time did we ever discuss Russia, Cuba, socialism or communism. Yet it was not long before the Center had been labeled "left-wing," "Communist," "dangerous," "subversive." My remarks to the students at the university added fuel to the fire and made the charge of communism more plausible. But we stuck it out, though ecclesiastical and political threats became irrational. Our people staged one large demonstration in San Juan directly in front of the new plush hotels, several of which have become gambling casinos and prostitution centers. Thousands of people from the States that day were inconvenienced because of our demand to be heard on housing, jobs, education, and health. Threats to the Center were increased in strength and numbers, but we continue to grow and we held out.

A group of desperate local people, middle-aged married couples, had been attending the Center. These people were among the hordes who fled to the States several years ago thinking that here they would find greater opportunity. Most of them went to the Washington-Baltimore-New York areas, and their experience was disastrous. They encountered slums and poverty worse than in La Perla, and for the first time in their lives were forced to endure restrictions and discrimination on the basis of race. For people who had never known a racial problem, life in the States was impossible for them to understand. They were despised because of their race and color and considered one grade lower than Negroes. So after several years of "grubbing" in the States, a number of these families returned to the island. One of the men who later came to our Center in San Juan said, "Life in the States did something destructive to me. It was not long before my wife, my children, and I began to hate people for no other reason than the color of their skin. When this happened, I said it was time for us to return to Puerto Rico, where though we live in poverty we do not live in hate."

Unknown to me and to all but one of the priests, four of these desperate families—disillusioned with life in the States and embittered by life in Puerto Rico—decided to attempt a sea journey to Cuba. Of course, such travel is as illegal from Puerto Rico as it would be from Florida. They made their way across the island to Aquadilla. There, under the cover of night, in a small fishing schooner, they set sail for Cuba, four hundred miles away. They never made it. They had been at sea not more than five hours when they were apprehended. They confessed their crime, were arrested, and are now being held as political prisoners.

79

The situation was complicated for me because one of our young priests attempted the trip with them! Since I was the director of the Center, the police arrested me and charged me with subversion—aiding Puerto Ricans, citizens of the United States, to escape to Cuba. I was convicted, given a suspended sentence, and paroled to my senior pastor, who promised the civil authorities that swift and severe disciplinary action would be taken. The Bishop of Puerto Rico called my Bishop in the States, and they agreed to an indefinite period of suspension and observation at Santa Bella. So here I am, waiting out the storm.

Sean

Part II
FINDING THE LIGHT

Cause for Celebration

Dear Sean,
   Wow!
   What a story. It is exciting to have a close friend who has been arrested and convicted for subversive activities! Of course, I have been called Communist by such men as Hank Bowers a number of times, but the epithet was more profanity than a serious charge. As Hal Luccock used to say, "Breathes there a preacher with soul so dead that his congregation has never thought him a little red?"
   During these months when I have been belly-aching and often feeling sorry for myself, you have been the one who has given me encouragement and kept my spirits up. And all this time you were carrying the weight of an arrest, conviction, and expulsion from a place you love. No wonder it has taken the establishment so long to make a decision. Now that I know the details, it will be even more interesting to see how the Church deals with your case.
   It is with some excitement that I write this letter, and confess I feel a little sheepish about it. Out of the blue, I received word from the Dean of my alma mater, Claymore Presbyterian College, that the faculty and trustees were awarding me the doctor of divinity degree (D.D.) this June. As you well know, I have complained about honorary degrees

83

and have criticized both donors and recipients. I also refused to address as Doctor any minister whose doctorate was a D.D. I have been kicked around, snubbed, and ignored for so long that I find this bit of recognition from my alma mater somewhat refreshing.

I considered refusing it, but then raised with myself the question of what was to be gained by this type of obstinacy. Claymore is one of our more liberal Presbyterian schools, and it has tried hard to live with the burning issues of our time. Why slap in the face those who make an effort to give recognition to a battle-scarred alumnus? Grace is pleased at the honor and says her husband deserves it. She tried out the "Doctor" last night, first verbally and then in writing, "Dr. Thomas Emerson Jones" or "Thomas Emerson Jones, D.D." She wants me to have the D.D. put on my stationery, but here I draw the line.

In my case I have the satisfaction of knowing that there was no wealthy member of my church on the board of trustees and no personal friend pressuring the board in my behalf. The Dean said that the degree was being awarded not because of any statistical success in the ministry but because of my forthright involvement with the pressing problems of our time. He further said that the college was not honoring me, but I would be honoring the college by accepting it. Those connected with Claymore were proud of a "minister alumnus" who refused to be browbeaten by the secular community. So I accepted the Dean's unexpected announcement in the spirit in which it was given. I must confess, however, that for one reason above all others I shall be forever grateful for the D.D. degree. Never again will I have to answer to "Reverend"! Authorities in etiquette quarrel over whether a minister should be addressed as "Reverend" or "The Reverend," the latter use prevailing. *I am equally repelled by both.* When people introduce me as Reverend Jones I feel outraged. Sometimes I stop them and suggest that they call me Pastor, which is also hard to take, but a shade better than

FINDING THE LIGHT

"Reverend." I've tried to teach my members to call me Mister, but in this I have miserably failed. Now I'll be Dr. Thomas Emerson Jones. After June 15 you may so address me!

Household news: "Mother" is a worshiper of Dr. Bobby Langley, who is holding a great revival and "Crusade for Christ" in Madison Square Garden. On Friday of last week a number of ladies in our church, her contemporaries and friends, chartered a bus to New York. They made the trip "Briar Wood night" and sat in special reserved seats. Two domestics from Smoketown who have not been swayed by black power and have recently been attending our church indicated that they would like to go. The chairman of the group suddenly announced that all space on the bus was taken. Well, anyway, they made the trip and "Mother" was saved—it was her third time, but she declares this one is real. To demonstrate the power of conversion she is a changed person around the house. No more quarrels with me and no more nagging Gail. This past weekend she was sugary sweet to Virginia, who hardly knew how to respond to the old lady. Of course she has always been sweet to Jim, her favorite grandchild. She is proud that her daughter married a minister, especially one who does not smoke. She prods Grace on preparing my favorite dishes, and when I come in at night—if she is up—runs to the door to greet me and then hurries to bring my house slippers. She criticizes Grace for not being nicer to me, and also reminds her that husbands do not live forever and that life without a man is indeed a lonely existence. This hostility switch from me to Grace has created a whole bag of new problems. For years Grace and her mother have had strong feelings toward one another. The problem is now out in the open. Not having experienced the mother-in-law bit, you haven't the slightest idea what I am talking about.

Saw Allen McCall in Philadelphia this morning, and he asked me to give you his regards. He was happy, proud, and cocky as ever. His Conference overwhelmingly voted him Bishop. However, the pastoral relations committee in his

85

mainline church begged him to turn down the election. Allen says they raised his salary to $30,000 a year, plus all benefits including the manse and a three-month vacation, plus a new Cadillac every year. In a tone of ministerial seriousness, he said that after much prayer and meditation he decided to remain with his church as an humble pastor. He and Jo will spend July and August in Switzerland.

Still no word from Tom. I could not stand the silence any longer. It has been more than three months. Several days ago I went to the Red Cross and they promised to check out his whereabouts for me. This anxiety has driven me to prayer when nothing else could.

Keep in touch.

Tom

The Myth of Disestablishment

Dear Dr. Thomas Emerson Jones:

Congratulations! And I do mean congratulations! I agree with the Dean—the college is not honoring you, *you* are honoring the college. For a long time you have been the conscience of Briar Wood, and it is about time someone recognized it. I agree with your remarks concerning "reverend" or "the reverend" or "the very reverend" or "the very most reverend." "Father" I can accept; the title implies a relationship which to me is meaningful. Concerning titles, a friend of mine, a Franciscan from England, explained something to me that I had never known. He says that physicians literally stole the title "Doctor" from ministers of religion, and did so soon after "Father" gained popular usage. For

86

hundreds of years "Doctor" was used only for distinguished men of the Church, especially pastors and teachers. The Latin word *doctor* means teacher. It has nothing to do with prescribing a pill or applying an ointment. My friend said that only recently in England has the physician been addressed as Doctor. So on good grounds I call you Dr. Jones.

Something you said in a letter several months ago prompts me to get off my chest my interpretation of organized or institutionalized religion. I have done my share of criticizing the establishment, but I hope it has always been, not in a spirit of malice, but as an effort to increase its effectiveness. When I called my Bishop a racist, I was not demanding an end to bishops and the hierarchy; I was simply saying in public that here was a man of God who by his life and ministry was expressing heretical views—views contradictory to the spirit of Christ Our Lord.

The establishment or the organization is easy to criticize and condemn. Any nonthinking, semirational, undeveloped person can do it. However, an idea remains nothing but an idea until it is organized. It takes the established forces of an institution to frame it and give it body and workability. The Communist theory of government is both naïve and childish, and it is to the credit of those in power in Communist countries that no one takes their basic theory seriously—I refer to the teaching that all forms of government will wither away, i.e., there will be no need of "organization" or "establishment" because a new man will have been created for the new order, and this new man will be of such a nature that he can live in freedom and responsibility minus institutions. It is a bit ironical that in states that have gone Communist there has arisen more organization and bureaucracy than is to be found in any other form of government!

But this same tendency toward organization and bureaucracy is to be seen in the capitalistic-democratic states—more and more government, not less and less. Such multiplication of organization is inevitable as nations become more highly populated. If one is marooned on an island with eleven other people, men, women, and children, chances are some sort of rules and regulations will have to be decided on— someone may even be forced to be the chairman! Or if one is thrown into a concentration camp with several hundred people who themselves must make decisions concerning eating, sleeping, working, and toilet privileges, organization in its most sophisticated form becomes the first priority. Langdon Gilkey's remarkable book *Shantung Compound* should be required reading for all contemporary critics in favor of doing away with organization. Here in 1943–44 were two thousand foreigners in China interned by the invading Japanese: people of various backgrounds—college professors, bankers, priests, nuns, missionaries. Gilkey, one of those held by the Japanese, not only describes in graphic detail both the heroic and the sinful behavior which such living produced among the inmates, but also makes the point that they could not have survived without careful organization. There had to be an "establishment" or an "institution." Two years in a small compound with two thousand people is a long time.

When we are trapped with more than two billion people on a miniature globe which is getting smaller by the year, and when these people are separated by regional and national boundaries, the refinements of government must be multiplied or life will come to an end. The task of enlightened man is not only to live with bureaucracy, but to improve it until it works for him rather than vice versa. Those who run organizations must know that they are responsible to the people they serve, rather than the opposite. There must be checks and balances in all forms of government, so that not only efficiency but justice can be done. The task of enlightened human kind, then, is not to destroy the establishment but to make it truly operative. Because of the frailty of man, there is no form of human life so easily corrupted as an institution of whatever kind. No wonder we often find ourselves saying in despair, "We can't live with it and we can't live without it!"

The possibility of private or public education remains an idea until someone provides the organization necessary to launching and sustaining it. The idea of democratic government remains an idea in someone's mind until it is "organized." The same principle is true with religion. If religion is to be more than a private mystical experience, if it is to involve both worship of a transcendent God and service to the *whole* man, then it must be organized, even as education and government. It will be institutionalized, it will have a hierarchy of some form or other, and it will develop an establishment.

One of my favorite Protestant authors is Professor Martin E. Marty. Just before leaving the States, I read his book *The New Shape of American Religion,* and I quoted freely from it when I delivered a paper to an ecumenical ministers' council in Patterson. The subject of my address was "The Myth of Disestablishment." In this paper I outlined all the familiar faults of institutional religion. But the point on which the presentation turned was a quotation from Professor Marty's book. I may not be able to give it verbatim—my books are still in Puerto Rico—but I remember the gist of it and do not believe I am misquoting in the following: "I view anti-institutionalism as a cheap solution to the problems of religion and emphatically disagree with the critics of organized religion. New iconoclasts would shatter the forms that centuries have developed and that the good sense of American people has brought to maturity." This is the strongest statement in defense of institutional religion I have ever read from a prominent Protestant leader. And I heartily agree with it.

I know you have been one to challenge the establishment, and I think this has been all to the good. But now the time has come not only to live with it, but to strengthen and improve it.

Sean

The Establishment Lives Again

Dear Sean,

When you say that worship of a transcendent God requires some sort of an establishment, I suppose you mean that such a God cannot do business with his subjects unless there is a group of fully trained, well-qualified, correctly commissioned individuals known as priests or ministers, who mediate His presence to the masses. At this stage, I am not sure that's true. However, when you say that if religion is to be more than a private mystical experience—and if it exists to serve the needs of the *whole* man—it must be organized, I can now accept that.

As you indicated, I have been a severe critic of the establishment. Boards, agencies, committees, secretaries, etc., simply had to be scrapped. Denominational executives were incompetent little men sending out reams of mimeographed letters begging for money and wasting the Church's resources. The mindless duplication of agencies by the various denominations was a shameful, extravagant disgrace. Moreover, the men who directed these impersonal boards and agencies were not in tune with the times—they were irrelevant. Most of them were so far removed from the human situation that they were little concerned about basic human needs—their chief concern was promoting another successful financial campaign.

My mind has somewhat changed. The other day I attended a meeting for laymen and ministers of the various denominations. The principal speaker was a Methodist denominational executive. He was everything else but a fat, ill-informed religious politician. He was youthful, full of ideas, straightforward, and enthusiastic. Some of the laymen present were

90

confused by what he said and some were angry; a few were appreciative. It seems that the Methodists have revamped many of their boards and committees, so that the work of the old-fashioned missionary has been updated and supplemented by ministries which are extremely relevant. He pointed out the types of new materials—books, journals, and magazines—which have been made available to the churches. The Methodist college magazine *motive* is as contemporary as one can get! Various boards have extended their mission to every area of underprivileged life. In addition to schools, colleges, and hospitals there are long-range programs for retarded children, magnificent homes for the aged, low-rent housing, and outpatient psychiatric clinics. Not only this, but the Methodists have become vitally and militantly concerned about war and peace. (Here the laymen became increasingly uncomfortable with the secretary's speech!) An agency to counsel young men who refuse to be drafted has been set up! A new thrust to the minority groups is being implemented, and starving children, not only in Biafra and India but in Mississippi, Alabama, Harlem, and the Appalachians will feel the concern of the "new" Methodist Church—not simply in terms of what the Church can do but in influencing the political power structures of the federal government. How irrelevant is a ministry whose leadership attempts to meet head-on the crucial problems of the day?

I chatted with the articulate secretary after the meeting, and he suggested that I look up some of the officials in my own Church and see what changes are taking place. I did so, and to my amazement I found that boards and agencies have in recent years undergone as radical a change as in the Methodist Church! You may think it strange that I have been so ill-informed about the new ministries. The explanation is simple. Since I gave up on the institutional Church several years ago, I have read no denominational journals. I have attended no meetings, not even those of the presbytery and synod. How could I know what was going on?

I had lunch the other day with Joe Farthing, pastor of Briar Wood Baptist Church. Joe has had his troubles with the hierarchy of the American Baptist Convention. To my utter surprise he described the same shift of emphasis in a number of boards and commissions at the Valley Forge Baptist Vatican (Joe's words). Executives have become militantly involved with the major issues confronting this nation. They have left their air-conditioned offices and have literally taken to soapboxes, speaking to pastors, laymen, and anyone who will listen. Boards are now offering local churches such programs of planning and strategy that if the congregations accept and implement them, the Church may be saved from extinction in our time. Joe also pointed out one other matter I would have been just as pleased not to have him mention. Leaders within our various denominations have been twenty-five years ahead of local congregations in facing head-on the tangled race problem. For instance, long before the Supreme Court decision of 1954, denominational officials were saying publicly and in print that local churches must open their doors to all people. Members and preachers in the churches simply would not listen to them!

I asked Joe if he felt the time will come when the boards will get so far from the local churches that there will be a definite split—the churches going in one direction and the denominational agencies in another. He feels this is a real possibility. If it should really happen, the ecumenical movement may be advanced by a hundred years! Progressive boards and commissions of the various denominations will merge, pool their efforts, and let conservative local churches go their way. Fortunately, most boards—this is especially true of the Baptists—have large independent incomes from invested funds. If local churches cease to support them, the boards will, of course, have to reduce the number of their ministers and go it alone. But they certainly would not go out of business. My Baptist friend feels that within twenty years the local, residential church will cease to exist as the norm for

Christian faith and action. Neighborhood churches will become museums and gathering places for the festivals of
Christmas and Easter.

To some extent my mind has been changed about the establishment, especially as it relates to the denominational
apparatus.

One more development to bring you up to date. Through
Hank Bowers, the John Birchers have at last gotten to a number of members of my congregation. Of course they seized on
my anti-Vietnam stand. Then the well-known Birch tactics
began. Foul, anonymous letters and telephone calls began to
come in, not only at church but on the half hour at home
throughout the night. I may have to get an unlisted number.
Grace is about to go out of her mind.

Tom

P.S. I must end this letter on the upbeat. Virginia graduated
from drama school last week. She has been signed to a singing
part in the off-Broadway musical, *Girls at Sea.* She has always
had an excellent voice, and we are proud of her. Grace and
I have tickets for the opening. Wish you were here to go with
us.

Being Relevant Can Be Deadly

Dear Tom,

Your new understanding of the establishment is appreciated. Don't cease to criticize it, but try to make it worka-
ble. You keep using the word relevant. There is one point in

Protestantism's eagerness to be relevant that bothers me. If relevance means yielding to the demands and desires of the people of a given generation, the church is really in trouble. New forms must prove themselves superior to old forms. But a guitar is not necessarily superior to a pipe organ, and the screeching and yelling of a rock singer is not comparable to a chorus singing Handel's *Messiah.* The cross as a symbol is still superior to a hubcap or a dollar sign.

Tradition has always been important to the Catholic Church. It has refused to bow to fads and fancies and has fought changes inspired by the whims of its people. Many changes have occurred in the life of the Church, but most of them unfortunately have been contrary to the spirit and teachings of Christ. They were often brought about for no other reason than to increase the power of the hierarchy, about which you and I have been so vocal. When changes in the Church occur, they should do so in the light of people's needs, not whims or fancies. *Drastic changes must occur today in the life of the Church, but these will not necessarily match the contemporary scene; they will approximate more nearly the simplicity we have in Christ rather than the pomp we have in the Vatican.*

When wishes and desires rule the practices of the Church in a given day, we may produce something similar to temple prostitution in the ancient city of Ephesus. I cannot believe that beautiful young maidens were reduced to religious prostitution in the temple because priests and religious leaders thought such practices were right. It was done because influential men found going to the temple to have intercourse with attractive young maidens a pleasant way to spend an afternoon or evening. *The temple became relevant!*

The craze for rock-and-roll music has at last reached the Catholic Church, but I predict that the Church will not easily budge on this matter. Rock and "country" music are not related to a historic religious event but to a musical fad, sometimes sentimentally religious. Before leaving Briar Wood I attended a service of rock music in Allen McCall's church. It was an overdose of banality; there is no other word to describe it but banal. The next week I showed up for a Lenten service in your stodgy old Presbyterian church. The magnificient choir that night sang several selections from the Messiah, and I was deeply moved. When rock can produce something equal to the Hallelujah Chorus, it will have won the right to be heard! But for God's sake let's not return to the cave of primitive man just because a mob prefers yelling and screeching banality.

You asked me to name some points where I am in disagreement with the Church. I don't mind doing so. *(a)* I disagree with the Church's official position on birth control. *(b)* I disagree with the Church's position on celibacy. Celibacy is not identical with a calling to the priesthood. Though I myself have made the decision to remain celibate, I consider celibacy highly impractical for most men. *(c)* I disagree with the Church's doctrine of infallibility. This is an instance where the Church Fathers very late in our history rammed through a specific act of ecclesiastical legislation to strengthen the weakened power of the hierarchy. It has now come home to haunt the whole Body of Christ. Papal infallibility in faith and morals is another word for idolatry. *(d)* I am opposed to the Church's concept of obedience. It is nonsense to tell a rational man that he must unquestioningly obey his superior— senior pastor or bishop or pope—if what has been ordered is cruel, stupid, violent, or just plain meaningless. Yet today this is precisely what the Church's doctrine of obedience means. All orders, good and bad, are to be obeyed because they have been handed down by one's superior. Of course this perversion is a violation of ancient Catholic teaching. I thoroughly agree with Father John A. O'Brien in the statement I quoted to the psychiatrist. Remember? "The enlightened conscience is the supreme court whose verdict is final and binding." I assure you that Father O'Brien's position is nearer to Catholic truth than is the doctrine of obedience now promulgated by the Church.

Am I a good Catholic if I find myself in such disagreement with Church policies and practices? Of course. Such disagreements have little to do with the core of a true Catholic's faith. Do I accept the Apostle's Creed? I do, every word of it. Do I accept as literally true the Nicene Creed. I do, every word of it. Do I accept the power and efficacy of the seven Sacraments? I do—every one of them! Is the bread and wine of the Holy Sacrament the Body and Blood of Christ? Yes, literally so, not figuratively or symbolically.

Well, that's enough about traditionalism and relevance. I'm sure you agree with me when I insist that relevance must never be thought of in terms of whims, fads, and fancies, but of human needs. If genuine *human needs* can be better met another way, then tradition must not prevent—but let us be sure we are dealing with *needs*.

Sean

SECTION THREE

A New Grace

Dear Sean,

OK, from here on I'll watch how I use the terms relevant and relevance!

As I told you in a recent letter, the Birchers have been trying to get me out of town. But their attempts—at least in one area—have backfired! Last Saturday night just as I was about to fall asleep, I heard Grace sobbing softly. She did something she has not done in years. She leaned over, put her arms around me, and kissed me. I calmed her down, and then she said, "Tom, can you ever forgive me? I've been so preoccupied with my own problems—my jittery feelings, the hot flashes, worrying about Tom in Vietnam, Virginia in New York, upset by Gail and her hippie ways and Jim and his stubbornness—and Mother, Mother most of all—I haven't realized what awful burdens you've been carrying."

Well, Sean, we both had a good cry and then in tender love we gave ourselves to each other as we have not done in years. Monday we checked out of the house—things would take care of themselves. We went to the Poconos and rented a beautiful cottage on a lake. Spring has come to Pennsylvania, and I must say it is not only early but magnificently beautiful. We stayed five glorious days—the first vacation we have had alone in fifteen years.

Know what she was crying about? It was not the change of life, it was the Birchers and their gross attacks on me. Here's what she said, "Those goddam bastards—are they Nazis trying to convert America into a police state? Oh, Tom, let's stay here and fight them!" Can you imagine Grace Jones, my southern, one-time Fundamentalist wife talking like that? Neither can I—but she's the new Grace.

The Birchers have outlined their plans and made them known to the entire community. They are determined to control libraries, censor plays, movies, and bookstores; take sex education out of the schools; dominate the local school board, intimidate schoolteachers, and frighten pastors. In addition to all this, they will fight the United Nations, fluoridation of water, the federal income tax, and above all the Supreme Court. But they have created a new wife for me and have brought us together. For this I can thank God!

"Mother" left yesterday. Though cool to Grace, she was sweet to me. She has gone to Atlanta. Grace's older brother is on the faculty of one of the colleges there, and he is a militant atheist. She has gone to live with him because, as she said to me, "He needs me more than you do."

The new birth is great.

Tom

Why Do They Ever Become Priests?

Dear Tom,

The news about Grace is wonderful, but it did not surprise me. I knew that she was real and that one day you would discover it all over again.

You ask me, "Why do men go into the priesthood?" The assumption in your question is that the priesthood, with its demand for chastity, poverty, and obedience, presents a young man with an austere life—is it worth it?

I must clarify one point about which many Protestants appear confused. *The vast majority of priests are in the priesthood because they profoundly feel that they have received a divine call to the religious vocation.* Furthermore, even with its hardships and demands, they love it. They would not trade it for any other work. It gives a man a feeling not so much of authority as of meaningful service in Christ's name. To sense the joy of worshipers who in Holy Communion take into themselves the very Body of Christ; to share in the joy of two young people, in love with each other and committed to Christ, who in marriage become one in the beginning of a new life together; to feel the security of a young married couple when the arms of Christ's Church are thrown about them as they present their new baby for baptism; to share in the emotional and spiritual relief that comes to the penitent in the confessional; to bring strength and reassurance to the sickroom, especially in terminal cases—to be at the bedside of a dying man or woman and in confidence administer the last rites—all this and more brings a dimension of meaning to one's life that is not to be compared with anything else. It is commonly thought that future priests are recruited by clever nuns or priests when they are young boys ten and twelve years of age, or that they are pressured into the priesthood by eager parents. To my knowledge this type of activity applies to only a very small group.

When one is at a place such as Santa Bella, lovely as it is, and rubs shoulders day after day with priests who are here for misconduct, one may get the impression that these poor fellows represent the priesthood. Nothing could be further from the truth. Tom, because of your open mind you have had the opportunity of knowing at close range far more priests than the average Protestant clergyman. How many of them were sex fiends, how many alcoholics, how many were crooked in their finances? My guess is that you have not known one priest who fits into any of these categories. No, the men who are having serious difficulties in the matter of morals are an infinitesimal number compared to the hundreds of thousands who wear the collar.

One other word about this small group of men who have moral lapses. Who is to say that their original calling was not from God? Because certain priests in adult life drink too much, is this any reason why in earlier life they should not have had a valid divine call? I think just the opposite is true. They heard the voice of God and felt His Spirit, and responded. Into the priesthood they went, with high hopes and spiritual idealism. As they grew older the pressures of celibacy, the "corruption" of the system (are not all systems corrupt?), and the complications and demands of the work turned them toward unacceptable avenues of escape. But let us not conclude that such men come into the priesthood without a divine calling or from low motives.

And nuns? God bless them! How maligned, how extravagant the descriptions of their lapses have been! The fact of the matter is that though nuns in the United States outnumber priests more than four to one, the violations of conduct would be an even smaller figure than among priests. Dedication, commitment, and consecration are the only terms in which to describe these wonderful people. To be sure, a number of nuns such as Marie are now forsaking the habit, but I make this point: when they decide that the perpetual life of the nun is not for them, they leave their orders—they do not remain and under the cover of secrecy carry on unacceptable conduct. But here again, compared with the total we are dealing with only a tiny number of women.

What about you? Why did you enter the ministry—how did you become a seminarian and a pastor? It was not to escape the draft and military service; it was not because you felt the ministry was an opportunity for great financial gain; it was not for anticipated prestige and honor. You became a minister because you experienced something resembling a divine call to the religious vocation. And furthermore, you were convinced not only that in answering this call you could more acceptably serve God, but that the ministry offered you an opportunity to serve the needs of God's people, both physical and spiritual.

Once again, I assume that there is a small percentage of men in the Protestant ministry such as Allen McCall, who thought he saw in the religious vocation an opportunity to advance himself—and he was not mistaken! But in all my life, Allen is the only Protestant minister of his kind I have ever known. I have known many with whom I strongly disagreed, on both religious beliefs and on social and political grounds. But my disagreement with them has little bearing on the sincerity of their calling and their work. I have never doubted or questioned that they were as committed as I.

I know how worried you are about Tom, Jr. In both my morning and evening prayers, I still remember him by name every day.

Sean

44377

The Ministry May Be for Real

Dear Sean,

    As you know, I have had difficulty finding reality in the work of a minister. My life in recent years has become so cluttered with trivial demands that I have been unable to see how near to the heart of human existence the minister lives. This week, in the midst of multiple and meaningless tasks, I had four experiences which make me feel a little more sympathetic to the ministry. First, I received a letter from a young married couple in their early thirties. This couple, with their one child, moved from Briar Wood several years ago— I had forgotten them. Before moving, the young wife in desperation came to see me. Her husband wanted a divorce. It was a familiar story: she had been cold, unresponsive, and demanding. However, she defended herself; she had not been prepared for marriage, sex is overrated, "My husband is impatient"— The husband later came to the office, and I found him to be an outgoing young man, full of energy and craving the warmth and affection of his wife. The more he pressed himself upon her, the more she withdrew into herself and away from him. He drifted into an affair with a fellow office worker. He admitted his indescretions. He did not want a divorce; he wanted reconciliation. I later talked to both young people, but have no notion of what I said. They went back together, moved from Briar Wood, and I had not heard from them until this week.

    Here is a portion of their letter,

DEAR REV. JONES,
You may not remember us, but this is the third anniversary of our reconciliation. We write to thank you for what you did when our marriage was on the rocks. You will never know how

101

much your interest in us and your understanding spirit did for
our home. You saved us from ourselves. We are now looking
forward to our second child, and we assure you that he (or she)
will be born into a family of love.
We shall be grateful to you always.

A note such as this sort of shakes you up.

Second, on Monday of this week I visited the oldest member of our congregation—a marvelous and spirited lady of
eighty-six! Mrs. Nabel has been married four times, outliving
each husband. She is now blind and a little deaf, but otherwise appeared in good strength. I seated myself directly in
front of her, and she said, "Old women in the congregation
think you have nothing else to do but visit them—I appreciate your coming, but believe me it isn't necessary. I told the
chairman of the board of elders that laymen and women in
the society ought to do more shut-in visiting." Then she said,
"I especially appreciate you, because you come laughing and
joking and not with Bible-thumping and a long face." Mrs.
Nabel could not stand my predecessor, because he was always trying to get her ready for death. When he left, she was
seventy-three and about to take a fourth husband!

She continued, "I've had my ups and down, my good times
and my bad times, but Pastor Jones, I remember with more
pleasure those moments when sweets were eaten in secret—
those were the times!" She took my hands in hers and said,
"You're a preacher, but you're a man before you're a
preacher. Never forget it. You're a real human being and
you've helped me a lot simply by being yourself. I love you
for it. Now I'm a little tired, death holds no terrors, I've drunk
deep of the waters of life, I want to go home."

Sean, that was Monday of this week. Tuesday night Mrs.
Nabel died, I conducted her funeral service yesterday. Believe me, I was near reality in the presence of this old lady.
I would not have missed knowing her for fame, fortune, and
a life of security.

The third experience also involved pastoral calling. Four

times a year I visit another remarkable woman in our membership. Her name is Betty Summerville, and she is now fifty-six years of age. When she was twenty and a junior in college, she was struck with a paralytic condition. The paralysis has extended throughout her body, including feet, legs, mouth, and throat. She can use her hands to propel herself around the house in a wheel chair. At her mother's death some years ago she inherited a small sum of money which barely keeps her alive. Her father deserted the family many years ago. Yesterday, when I saw her, Betty was happy and could hardly control herself. For years she has lived alone, but now a brother whose wife died recently has come to live with her. She wrote on a piece of paper—she cannot speak—that every day she prepares Bill's evening meal. This is the greatest thing that has ever happened to Betty. Bill does the marketing and the housecleaning; Betty gets his supper. In the early morning she struggles to bathe and dress herself (this takes hours), then begins the event of the day—preparing the evening meal for her brother. Life has not been very good to Betty Summerville. Mother dead, no father, no husband, no children, and few friends. Nothing but a wheel chair existence for thirty-six years. Yet there has never been a trace of self-pity or bitterness. Here is one soul whose life has been refined in the fires of human suffering.

The fourth experience occurred last night about midnight. Grace and I enjoyed a late snack and were planning ways of combatting the nuisance of the Birchers when the phone rang. It was the wife of my militant, right-wing member, Hank Bowers.

Amy was hysterical. I hurried over to the Bowers house and found temperance elder Hank Bowers bleary-eyed, drunk, and vicious. Amy was coherent and said, "We got word late this afternoon that Roy has been killed in Vietnam." She put her face in her hands and cried, "My God—what'll we do, what'll we do?"

Hank started drinking soon after the news came. Who is to

blame him? How does a man take the news that his nineteen-year-old son and only child has been killed in a war that has no meaning? He was drunk, but he could still express himself. Those men wounded, those deaths you hear about on TV had been statistics to him, just numbers—but now it was his son Roy. Hank said he had begun to have doubts about the wisdom and the necessity of our involvement in Vietnam soon after Roy left but he had kept it to himself. Now he was sick of the whole Vietnam war. He had got out his rifle, loaded it, and was vowing drunkenly to kill the President of the United States, the Secretary of Defense, and the Secretary of State.

He looked me straight in the eye and said, "I've tried to destroy you. I got the Legion and the Birchers on your tail. Can you forgive me? *You* have a son in that goddam mess. Is there no way we can get him home?"

What do you say in a high-pressure emotional situation like this? I'm often tongue-tied and flounder for words. Hank Bowers' son was dead and Hank Bowers, my mortal enemy, puts his arms around me, weeps, and asks my forgiveness. It broke me up.

Amy asked if I would stay with them for the rest of the night, and I did. Hank slept fitfully, but in the morning he was clear-headed and grim. He knew what had happened and he was still aware of our conversation. He accepts his son's death with bitterness, but is genuine in offering me his friendship.

I suppose a minister must learn that if he is going to live this close to the raw realities of people's lives, he must be prepared to accept the trivialities and the nonsense that goes with the job.

So in the midst of much that is trivial and meaningless, there are some rewards.

Tom

P.S. What in heaven's name is happening in the Roman Catholic Church? Yesterday's *Times* carried the headline, 31 BROOKLYN PRIESTS RENOUNCE DIRECTIVE BY POPE ON

104

CELIBACY. The report quoted the priests, "While we ourselves have no intention of marrying at this time, we are setting ourselves against the directives of the Pope and the Bishops on the question of celibacy."

These are fantastic developments. Are the decisions at Vatican II responsible?

The Church and the Pocket of Neglect

Dear Tom,

Your description of finding the vein of reality in your work stirred me. It's there. We just have to find it. I've looked deep into too many frightened eyes and sorrowing faces ever to want anything but the ministry of the Church.

You ask my opinion of the impact of Vatican II. The answer is not difficult. The tragic death of John F. Kennedy killed a generation of youthful idealism, not simply in the United States but around the world. The death of Pope John prevented many of the hopes and dreams of progressive Church leaders from being realized. Nevertheless, Vatican II has stirred the Church at its foundations, and there is no turning back. The matter of ecumenicity has gone further than Pope Paul really wishes—Catholics, Protestants, and Jews are joining for worship and action. Priests are assisting in Protestant weddings and vice versa. The demand and promise concerning children born of a mixed marriage was changed by the Council from a statement in writing to a verbal statement. The truth of the matter is that few priests anywhere require even the verbal statement.

A stronger position might have been taken on religious liberty. The Catholic Church will never be free until it can stand financially by itself throughout the world. It should not seek or accept preferential treatment from any government, including Spain, Ireland, and Italy. It should cease to be a state Church in any country. The post-Vatican pronouncement by Pope Paul on birth control was a tragic blunder. It violated the needs of our people, virtually all of whom are now forced to ignore it. The Vatican did not even discuss celibacy. This, the Church has since discovered, was a mistake. Celibacy must be discussed, and celibacy as a requirement for all men who seek the priesthood will someday be lifted. To the dismay of Pope and bishops, the Church in Holland is leading the way in sensible reform. It simply ignores many of the rigid, untenable demands of the Vatican. It has dispensed with practices of the Church which were once innovations and later became traditional—such traditions as papal infallibility and celibacy, for instance, which have nothing to do with the teachings of Christ or the spirit of the early Church.

These are my feelings about some of the recommendations and actions of Vatican II. However, I am at present more concerned about what I call the great pocket of neglect. Namely, the life of the Church in the midst of poverty. The Church is concerned about *faith*, whether it is heretical or true. *Actions* must also be judged by the same standard— heretical or true? Racial discrimination, for instance, is heretical when judged by the spirit of Christ. Living in wealth, extravagance, and splendor in the midst of grinding poverty is also heretical. This is more serious than the acceptance or rejection of the Pope's encyclical on birth control. In all countries, but especially in Latin America, the Church has been slow to interpret its responsibility to poverty-stricken peoples. What happened in Mexico a number of years ago is likely to be repeated in many Latin American countries. After the Mexican revolution the Church was not closed, but properties were confiscated and the activity of priests and nuns severely restricted. The hierarchy has no voice and little influence in affairs of state. The Church cannot continue to live with its own extravagance and affluence in the midst of starvation, slums, poor education, and poor medical services.

There are two ways in which the Church can confront the crises of poverty: both are important. In many countries, she would do well to sell her jewels and other costly possessions. Priests and those in the higher echelons of the hierarchy could live on a reduced scale, thus sharing deeply in the poverty of the people. By these savings the Church could distribute to the poor the goods and possessions she has hoarded through the years. In identifying with the people in this way, she would in turn save her own soul.

Second, in those countries where the Church still exercises some influence in affairs of state (the number is dwindling), priests, bishops, archbishops, and cardinals should press upon ruling governments the necessity of meeting the crises of poverty NOW. The hierarchy should encourage peaceful assembly and peaceful demonstrations such as we sponsored in San Juan. It should work quietly behind the scenes with officers of government and constantly press them to enact measures to relieve the scourge of poverty. You know as well as I what usually happens. If the Church is not bothered by government interference, if it is permitted to go its own way, if it is supported out of national tax revenues, Church officials are only too happy to cooperate with authorities and say nothing and do nothing to upset the status quo. This is religious heresy! It is contradictory to the spirit of Christ Our Lord, who constantly identified himself with the needs of the poor.

When resources are available, why must a country stall and wait until there is bloodshed or a revolution before doing something daring and creative to combat large pockets of poverty? The idle life at Santa Bella has set me to worrying afresh about Puerto Rico and its future. The economy of the Commonwealth is tied to the economy of the States. As a result of Vietnam and other factors, inflation is rampant. Food prices, rents, etc., are fantastically high. Workers—those who have jobs—cannot survive on their weekly wages. The slums of La Perla and the conditions in the southern villages stand as an indictment of the life of affluence in the midst of poverty. Must violence and bloodshed occur before the "fat cows" bestir themselves? Must revolution take place before the Church genuinely shows her compassion for the conditions of the people?

So, as to the various sessions of Vatican II: some good things were accomplished, but many issues were not faced. However, in considering the "new" Church, I am nore interested in its willingness and ability to confront poverty—the great pocket of neglect—then I am in statements of faith.

Sean

SECTION FIVE

Freedom—the Shield of Illusion

Dear Sean,

Guess who showed up in Briar Wood this week?

Julian Feldman!

He came by the church study and we had a three-hour, old-time bull session. He looked haggard and worn, and was extremely apologetic about not writing either of us. He said rather dejectedly, "How could I write? What did I have to say?"

Julian resigned his position as editor of the *News* early last month. He has seen several rabbis in New York and has talked to the president of the synagogue here in Briar Wood. He has been gone nearly five years. His successor at Beth Israel resigned in February, and they have been looking for a replacement. Julian indicated to me that he has been offered his old job and is likely to accept. Of course I am excited about this.

Without my asking, he confessed that he wrote the right-wing editorials I told you about. His story was simple and to some extent understandable. He left the rabbinate because freedom of expression was being denied him. For several months he quietly looked for a job where he would have fewer restrictions and greater latitude. He had had considerable writing experience, so decided to hunt for a newspaper job. But what newspaper? To do his best work he had to find one with a liberal point of view. Since most papers in this country are owned by wealthy, conservative men, this would not be easy. Quite by accident he landed the job in Connecticut.

The *News*, he felt, was in the liberal tradition and would give a man of his persuasion considerable opportunity for expression. Mr. Barnard Burlingame was the noted owner and publisher; his liberalism dated back to Franklin Roosevelt, whom he vigorously supported. An autographed picture of the former President hangs in his office. He campaigned for Harry Truman, John F. Kennedy, and Lyndon Johnson. Most of the staff, including reporters, shared the old man's point of view. So in a way the paper was one big happy family.

Julian accepted the job as reporter and things went well. As you know, he is exceptionally bright, and it was not long before he was promoted to a desk job—assistant editor, then associate editor, and last year editor-in-chief. At forty-one he was top man on one of the most respectable daily papers in New England. But did he find freedom?

Julian said that to get the job as editor-in-chief and keep

it for a year, he sold his soul and sacrificed whatever integrity he had. The publisher became the victim of two serious back-lashes. Together, both of them smashed whatever liberal views he may still have cherished. Black power and its evils became an obsession with the old man. According to him, blacks in this country have gone crazy. They don't appreciate what good men have done for them. They talk about seizing political and economic power, and many of them resort to violence to get what they want.

Also, the old man was a fanatical supporter of President Johnson and his Vietnam policy. "Lyndon Johnson is a greater president and more liberal than Franklin D. Roose-velt," he said privately and in print. The more public opinion turned against the President, the more furious he became in defense of the administration. He became an extremist. No one could say a word in defense of the aims of black people, and no one could write a word of criticism of the Vietnam war. Even reporters had to censor or slant their articles to make them conform to the publisher's policy.

Where did all this leave Julian who had given up his pulpit to find freedom of expression? In the early days of his newly acquired position as editor-in-chief, he took a chance and wrote an editorial on "Vietnam—America's Lost Cause" in which he pointed out the extent of the black market in South Vietnam, the lack of will of the people, and the unreadiness of the South Vietnamese army to defend them. Not counting half a million U.S. fighting men, tanks, and jets, the South Vietnamese army alone numbers *twice* the size of the Viet-cong and the forces of North Vietnam. The editorial raised the question: With all these superior troops in the field, why can't the Vietcong be defeated in a matter of weeks?

Mr. Burlingame called Julian to his office. Over his desk the old man shouted, "Either you begin to make sense out of your editorials on the blacks and the Vietnam war, or you can get the hell out of here right now."

For once in his life, Julian was up against something he

could not cope with—a hard-core, thoroughly secular man who held in his hands the power of life and death over his employees. Married, with three children, two of them in college, what was he to do? After leaving the rabbinate over a disagreement with synagogue officials, a confrontation with his present employer would be disastrous. Where would he turn? Who would hire a man with a record like that?

He put his head in his hands and cried, "I sold out—what else could I do?"

For an entire year he turned out material directly contradictory to what he believed: "Black people are moving too fast." "The war in Vietnam is in defense of our own national security." "The poor among us are poor because they will not work." Etc. At the end of the year he resigned as editor-in-chief. Julian found that there was more freedom in the pulpit at Beth Israel than at the *News!* He is returning as the rabbi of his flock, a chastened, nearly broken man.

You will be interested to know that Gail, now seventeen has given up her weekend hippie-yippie bit on two grounds. First, she has become quite a capitalist, making $2.50 an hour baby-sitting! It sounds like extortion to me, but that's what high-school girls are demanding these days. Second, she says that the kids going to the East Village from Briar Wood and surrounding communities on a Saturday are thirteen and fourteen years old. The generation gap between a thirteen-year-old and a seventeen-year-old is the greatest gap of all! Besides, she has settled down to going steady with a Benjamin Franklin senior, captain of the basketball team, who will not tolerate yippie nonsense.

Let me hear from you soon.

                                             Tom

P.S. I forgot to tell you that Julian knows personally the man who is president of the real estate firm where I said I was going to work the first of September. To my horror he says

111

that this man—not a politician—practically originated the statement, "A man's home is his castle," and is the chairman of a state real estate organization very similar to the white Citizens' Councils in the South!

Food Which the World Cannot Give Nor Take Away

Dear Tom,

Good old Julian!

He discovered the hard way that absolute freedom is difficult to come by. How well I remember, when I first went to Puerto Rico, my humiliating experience on becoming involved in the Münoz political struggle. As I mentioned to you, I publically supported Münoz and his efforts to establish birth-control clinics against the demands of the Bishop—who was enraged by my efforts and declared he would hold the senior pastor responsible for my conduct. The old pastor was one of the most gentle souls I have ever known. He had treated me like a son. What was I to do? At the risk of destroying the pastor and myself, I could have continued my attacks on the Bishop's program as well as public support of the Governor, but I didn't. I ceased all activity and during the remainder of the political campaign kept my mouth shut. It nearly killed me, but I did it, and I have not ceased to feel unclean because of my lack of forthrightness and courage at a time when so much was at stake for the people of Puerto Rico.

Private meditation and reflection have given me deeper insight into my own personality as well as the life of the Church. More and more I miss the privilege of saying Mass every day. More and more I grow restless because I am for-

112

bidden to partake of the Holy Eucharist. One whose life, strength and very soul has been nourished by the Body and Blood of Christ cannot easily dismiss this experience. I know you will not take offense when I say that Protestants have often given me the impression that Communion is for them a monotonous and casual ritual—a symbol or a memorial, nothing more. According to my faith and experience, to reduce the Eucharist to a symbol and memorial is to destroy it and the substance of life it brings to mortal man. The Eucharist must be the Body and Blood of Christ, the daily offering and sacrifice of Christ for the sins of the world, the food of life for God's people.

I have known too many people who came to the altar and took to themselves the bread of Christ. These were people overwhelmed by the harshness of the world in which we live. They were frightened by the uncertainties of life and the certainty of death. They were weak and afraid. But at the rail, Christ entered into them afresh, and His love and strength became their love and strength. They walked away from the altar different persons from what they were when they came. To be the minister of Christ, to partake of His life and share that life with His people is to me more than ever man's highest privilege. I wish it were possible for you to allow the Eucharist to mean more than "symbol," more than "memorial," more than "remembrance." Let it mean all that Our Lord meant for it to mean, when he said, "Unless you eat the flesh of the Son of man and drink his blood, you have no life in you; he who eats my flesh and drinks my blood has eternal life ... for my flesh is food indeed and my blood is drink indeed. He who eats my flesh and drinks my blood abides in me and I in him."

Will we ever see each other again? For a variety of reasons it is best that I shouldn't return to Briar Wood or to the East. Is there any chance that you and Grace might get to the West Coast? What a reunion we would have!

Sean

Does the Depth of Man's Sin Demand God?

Dear Sean,

It is not possible for me to think of Holy Communion in the way you describe in your last letter. I can understand how one who is born, so to speak, in the faith and trained from childhood to respond to the Eucharist could see in it the actual body and blood of Christ. Believing this, such a person would naturally feel that Christ had entered into him in a real way. In my darker moods, I have looked upon this practice as "sacred cannibalism"; in my brighter moments I have interpreted Communion as symbol and as memorial.

However, yesterday (Sunday) I had a most unusual experience while administering the sacrament. As you know, I have never been given to mystical experiences, and what I now describe is far from that category. However, when one suddenly views a certain aspect of life from a wholly new perspective, when he catches a vision so that conclusions previously held are radically changed, I suppose such an experience may be classified as "mystical."

I am confident that yesterday's experience was inspired or produced by my having recently read two remarkable books. The first was the anguished autobiography of a famous British clergyman, D. R. Davies, who began his clerical career as a Congregational minister. It was not long until he drifted into humanism, agnosticism, and atheism. He left the clergy, became fanatically involved in the great causes of the day, always taking the left-wing or liberal position. For a short time he entered politics and supported socialist causes. In 1937 he went to Spain and saw firsthand "the ghastly tragedy of Spain's great Civil War. The terror-stricken refugees, the lean faces of little half-starved children and the pathetic sto-

114

lidity of young men about to die."

Years later, in a moment of self-examination, Davies recovered a dynamic faith in God. He says, "Ultimately, one does not find God until one is stripped of every rag and deprived of every support, and stands alone. In that final anguish, God becomes inevitable."

Davies' return to religion did not originate in a new understanding of God, but in a new understanding of man. He saw man not in any way endowed with "inner powers of goodness," but as a wild, depraved creature whose aggressive energies must not be stifled but redirected toward the common good. He writes, "Imagine a world of men with an ape soul, but the mind of a technician! That is the horror to which forgetfulness of a Creator, Sovereign God has exposed humanity. The possibility of such a hell has already emerged into history. Jonathan Edwards' lurid descriptions of a Hell beyond death were a picnic compared to the Hell which unredeemed, omnipotent man can create in this life." Davies refers to man as a "radical sinner" in need, not of superficial salvation, but of "radical redemption."

So a man made the circle from timid believer to liberalism, to agnosticism, to atheism, and all the way to a new faith and a new relation to the Church. A man past middle age, Davies was ordained a clergyman in the Church of England, where he remained until his death a few years ago.

The burning question in my mind: Do the depths of man's sin demand the existence of a God capable of dealing with that sin?

The second book I read last week which had a powerful effect on me was Camus' *The Fall.* Camus, as no other modern writer, has penetrated to the core of man's wickedness. As I read him, he has no solution, no word of hope for man—the only way out is suicide. He appears to agree with Robert Penn Warren, who wrote, "There's no forgiveness for being human. It is the inexpugnable error. It is ... the one thing we have overlooked in our outrageous dreams

115

and cunningest contrivances."

Sean, could there be an interlocking system in man's evil, so that man becomes guilty, if not by overt acts of greed and aggression, then by default—just by being human? When mighty bombs are dropped in Vietnam, when villages are napalmed and old women and little children incinerated as if they were in the gas ovens of Buchenwald, am I less guilty than the youthful hand that pulled the lever releasing those bombs? No, a thousand times no! I am part of a ghastly system which I support with both strength and money.

The starkest fact of human existence is that all of us are caught in the network of darkness. If a man does not sin with his genitals, he sins with his spirit. Years ago I asked myself the question, "Does this approach to man's sin destroy his freedom." In my more liberal years I answered Yes, and immediately discarded the notion that man's nature is innately evil. John Calvin, whom I threw out the window upon graduation from seminary, has come back by the front door. An examination of what Calvin meant when he spoke of depravity might shake us all up.

Camus in *The Fall* suggests that men are capable of unlimited greed, aggression, cowardice, pride, violence, and peacock self-centeredness. Like vultures, they feed off one another. But he offers no suggestion as to how we got that way, nor any solution to our desperate plight.

Thank God, Camus does not make the mistake of Communists who insist that men are evil because they are victims of evil institutions. Correct, destroy, or change the institutions and you change man. A new man will be born for the new order. Officiating at Communion yesterday I saw, as never before, that there is a destructive principle endemic in man. Institutions do not corrupt man; he corrupts institutions. Governments do not corrupt man; he corrupts governments. The Church does not corrupt man; he corrupts the Church. The deep flaw within his nature, the will to power and aggressive-

116

ness, the mighty thrust toward greed and self-centeredness, stalk his daily existence.

I looked into the faces of the people who made up my congregation—fear, anxiety, pride, selfishness, all were there. But Sean, in that brief moment I did not see Hank Bowers or any of the other hundreds of people whose lives are caught in the web of evil—*I saw myself, Tom Jones.* For the very first time in my life I sensed my involvement with human sin. *These are my people—in sin I am one of them.* I, too, know the meaning in my own life of greed, aggression, cowardice, vanity, violence, and self-centeredness. To sense this is to experience a crushing feeling of terrible weight— a weight I am unable to carry.

Does man's sin demand a faith in a moral God of redeeming love? Certainly peace of mind does not require it—I may arrive at peace of mind by any one of several avenues, including the inheritance of a bundle of money. Does working for a better society demand a faith in God? I believe not. Thousands upon thousands of people work every day for better conditions among men, with no thought of God. Does the visible fact of Creation demand an affirmation of God? I think not. The Creation could well be the product of superenergy, nothing more. Certainly it does not demand an affirmation of a loving, forgiving God. Does the fear of death and the hope of life after death demand an affirmation of God? *Certainly not from me.* I am not even sure I believe in life after death. What is it that demands of me a response to and faith in God? Radical evil within me in terms of greed, aggression, violence, pride, hate, lust, self-centeredness—these cry out for help, relief, control, redemption. Who ministers to my condition? *Flower power?* Flowers fade and only disillusionment is left. *Education?* Many of Hitler's storm troopers were Ph.D.'s. *Social conditions?* In terms of bitterness, disillusionment and unrest, the Scandinavian countries (for which I have a profound admiration) are no better off than England, France, the

117

United States. What about *psychiatry?* Psychiatrist, cure thyself! The vast majority of practicing psychologists and psychiatrists with whom I have dealt in the past twenty years have been men and women as mixed up as the rest of us! These practitioners say man's unacceptable behavior is due to the misuse of his freedom, or to a mother who rejected him. Or the enlightened are now sure that environment, his institutions, make man what he is. *But what makes the psychiatrist what he is?* Should he not know better? Should he not be better? A psychiatrist friend of mine caught his wife in bed with a college boy and shot both wife and lover to death.

If man is to become truly human, he will do so only in joyful reunion with Him who created him and who by the cross extends His unlimited love in terms of reconciliation. Man can know the power of God's forgiveness. Only then will the terror of his nature be curbed and his thrust for selfish power channeled into a will-to-power for others. Only then will his claws be trimmed and his spirit empowered by love—real *agape* love.

I said the words, "This is my blood of the new covenant which is shed for many for the remission of sins." I saw my congregation, and I didn't see them—I saw Tom Jones, an evil man in need of God's love. A critic of Christianity once facetiously said, "It is God's business to forgive sins." I now say, it is not only His business (who else can do it?) but it may be His chief business.

I feel that I am on the verge of something new and great —am I a lost man who has been found, a dead man who has been made alive?

Tom

P.S. Voltaire once said, "When men begin most to talk about God, they then begin to act like the Devil." It may be a risk worth taking.

The Possibility of Self-control and Sublimation

Dear Tom,

Augustine and Calvin were not too far apart in their interpretation of the nature of man! I will accept either.

Some time ago you asked me a question which I have delayed answering. It revealed the mind-set of many Protestants toward the priesthood.

You asked, "What do priests do for sex?" Many Protestants are quite sure that priests do not do without sex; they get it somewhere. I derive little pleasure from destroying erotic thoughts of Protestants concerning our sex lives, but the truth is, we do nothing. The vast majority of priests, especially those who have come through the teen and young adult years, find pleasure and satisfaction in ways other than sexual. This does not mean that we are entirely ignorant in the ways of sex. We know about masturbation, nocturnal sex dreams, and contacts with animals. We are aware of the life of fantasy and the power of the imagination. We also know the world of the homosexual; however, only a small, a very small number of our men fall into such activity. In all my years in the priesthood I have never known a fellow student or priest to make what might be termed a homosexual gesture.

I find myself in disagreement with many of the untold number of sex laws of the Church. Masturbation—male and female—is a sin, nocturnal dreams are not a sin if you did nothing to stimulate them, they are sinful if you stimulated them; all forms of oral sex are evil; sex without procreation as the intent is unacceptable, withdrawal prior to a climax is sin that must be confessed, all artificial means of birth control are wicked, mouth kissing is reserved only for the engaged or the married, tongue kissing is extremely wicked (if the tongue is inserted into the partner's mouth a short distance, it is less a sin than if deep), all forms of abortion, even when a girl is

119

raped by her father, are also sinful. Homosexuality, male and female, by mutual consent or otherwise, and in whatever form, is condemned.

"Priests get sex from willing nuns."

"Priests get sex from their housekeepers."

"Priests have intercourse with single women in their parishes who are susceptible."

"Priests get sex from frustrated and embittered married women who live with indifferent husbands."

"Men enter the priesthood because they have strong homosexual drives and can find there a protective shelter for their activity."

"Priests get sex from contacts made in the confessional."

Tom, your people are wrong—they have vivid imaginations, but in ninety-nine cases out of a hundred they are dead wrong!

I know how much the pleasure of sex has meant to you—and I suppose, in some way, I envy you for your interest and your capabilities. My guess is that you will keep going strong until you are eighty. However, I'm pretty sure my own sex drive is also strong. If I slept in a bed, unclothed, with the woman I love, also unclothed and could touch and smell her, my frequency would be pretty high!

But I tell you something now that will be difficult for you to believe. Marie and I met and fell in love. We often had long sessions of intimate conversation after school hours—in the classroom, in my office, sometimes at night when we drove around in my car. For nearly a year we met secretly in the beautiful, isolated home of her parents outside of Princeton. We sang and played records. We caressed and kissed and made great plans for our marriage—but get this: not once were we ever intimate. Yet we knew what love and passion are. When two people make up their minds to save the best until after the wedding, they can, with self-control and determination, do it. Early teaching and training as well as psycho-

120

logical conditioning made our having premarital intercourse
an impossibility.

I want to say a word about the possibility of sublimation
and offer an explanation of why so many priests do not need
sex. As I indicated to you, a small percentage of men in the
hierarchy unquestionably derive some pleasure out of discussing the minutiae of sex and passing detailed sex laws.
This in some way relieves their repressions. But there are not
very many of them. The bulk of the leaders in the Church are
priests like myself. I assure you, we rarely sit on commissions
to determine the rightness or wrongness of sexual practices!
And we derive little pleasure from reading about these laws
in detail. No—if pleasure is experienced, satisfaction
achieved, it is in and through the work of the Church. This
becomes an obsession with us. From early morning until late
at night, we are *emotionally* involved with the problems of
human existence—birth, marriage, terminal illness, death,
domestic problems, vocational problems, problems of faith.
The priesthood is currently caught up in a great struggle
against every form of injustice. This includes racial discrimination, slums, poor housing, poor health facilities—the whole
gamut of problems arising out of poverty. When priests,
young and old, give themselves in reckless abandon to people
and the conditions that surround them, there is no overwhelming need for sex. Energy has been magnificently sub-
limated from one concern to another.

I have several friends who are creative artists. One man, a
novelist, tells me that when he is writing furiously every day,
week after week, month after month, he hardly thinks about
sex. He has neither the interest nor the capacity for sexual
contacts. This condition may last four or five months. When
he ceases his creative labors, he turns toward a woman for
sexual release on a daily basis! The same is often true of those
who work on canvas, or the man who writes music or practices five, six, seven hours a day with an instrument. They
have discovered that sex energy is related to various forms of

emotional energy. When emotional outlets are fully provided by one set of interests, sex is not needed.

Here is an illustration: As you know, when I work, I work like a demon (I hope, angel)—ten, twelve, fourteen hours a day. Here at Santa Bella, I have been forced into a continuous state of inactivity, the relaxed life. In many ways it has done me a lot of good. But the irony is that, with the quiet life, I have few outlets for my emotions. Thus, since I have been confined in this lovely place I have had more difficulty with sex than at any time since I was in my late teens. Powerful urges to masturbate, nocturnal sex dreams, and a fantasy life, wild and uninhibited, have gripped me. Once I am out of here, once I am doing the work of the Church, this condition will disappear as dew before the morning sun.

Tomorrow is the day! The Father Superior returned from Rome this morning. I was informed at lunch that I am to have my conference with him tomorrow morning at eleven o'clock. Excited and can't wait. I'll give you the word.

Sean

P.S. I am no woman-hater, as you well know. But I think women seeking financial security have kept alive the myth that men could not live without them. What they have to offer by way of sexual intimacy and release is absolutely indispensable to the poor creature called man. This is a myth, and thousands upon thousands of our men in the priesthood are living proofs of it.

Have We Lost Each Other Again?

Dean Sean,

This is my third letter to you in three weeks and I have had no reply.

On the envelope of this letter you will notice I have written *Please forward—Important.*

It is difficult for me to imagine why I have not heard from you. It is five years since you left Briar Wood. Have we lost each other again? Are you still at Santa Bella? Have you gone to Mexico, the South Sea Islands, or Africa? Are you ill?

Grace says that before you accept another assignment you *must* come East for a visit, regardless of your Bishop—or, for that matter, regardless of anything that has happened in the past. Now that "Mother" is gone we have an extra bedroom. We promise to leave you free to do anything you want. All we hope for is to see you, talk to you, visit the Rathskeller together and enjoy your company.

We anxiously await a word.

Tom

Sean Got The Shaft

Dear Tom,

The conversation on the phone last night was not at all satisfactory. I am so upset that it is difficult for me to make myself clear. I should not have called. Under these circumstances I can express myself much better in writing. But it was good to hear your voice again. Grace sounds wonderful, and I'm glad I got to speak to both Gail and Virginia. Gail sounds like a grown woman. She hopes to be accepted at Barnard when she graduates? I can't believe she's that old! And Virginia—what a treat to talk to her! She is a capable, determined young lady. Certainly none of the artificial tones and inflections so common to those in the acting business seem to have rubbed off on her. She's a *real* person. I know you are proud of her. Did I understand her to say she is getting married in June? To an actor? What a lucky man!

Here's my story in cold black and white.

The heavens have fallen. I have been excommunicated—the word itself has a harsh and horrible sound. Not that I fear hell and damnation, but the thought that I am forever separated from the work that was my life is devastating. I cannot yet take in the full meaning of what has happened. I am forty-one years old, nearly forty-two, and I began the study for the priesthood when I was sixteen. So for twenty-five years I have known nothing else. What do I do now? Where do I turn?

The day after my conference with the Father Superior (three weeks ago) I was handed $150 by one of the minor officials in the retreat office, instructed to leave my cell in order, to turn in whatever books I had withdrawn, and to be off the premises by noon. My cell for the moment is an unsightly room in a cheap hotel in downtown San Diego. I am dressed in street clothes, including a plain summer sport shirt. My clerical collar I left behind; never again will I wear it. I know something of the feelings of "the man without a country."

As best as I can, I will reconstruct for you my conference with the Father Superior. I was ushered into his presence promptly at 11:00 A.M. It was a surprise to see His Eminence at close range. I caught a glimpse of him once at a distance as he walked across the courtyard, and at that time he appeared rather young, at least in the middle age category. And I thought I caught a trace of sternness, perhaps even coldness. Now I was in the presence of an elderly man at least seventy years of age. His rich, full head of hair was snow white and his face wrinkled as if weatherbeaten. But—get this—there radiated from his personality a gentleness which touched me and which I shall not soon forget.

In a soft, pleasant voice he asked me to be seated. The momentary stillness was the stillness of death. We both remained quiet for what seemed an eternity. As if he had memorized what he would say to me, at last he spoke. I think I can reconstruct for you most of what he said.

"You have been under serious study for a number of years. In fact, since you embarrassed your Bishop in Briar Wood, your superiors have been in touch with the Holy Father concerning your case. It was the Vatican that suggested that you be sent to Puerto Rico where you would be under the authority of a Bishop known over the Catholic world as a strict disciplinarian.

"You had hardly arrived in the Commonwealth when you publicly disagreed with your new superior. Following this came the news of your debate or lecture at the university, in which you recommended that the government of the United States recognize the atheistic government of Fidel Castro. Then you opened the 'center of Christian Action,' which turned out to be a subversive organization assisting Communist elements on the island. Then in violation of the laws of the government of the United States, you assisted a number of families, including one young priest, to attempt the voyage to Cuba."

Tom, I did not interrupt by attempting to offer His Eminence a counter-explanation. By this time I knew what was coming and tried to prepare myself for it.

"Your confinement at Santa Bella has been longer than in

most cases. If this has caused you any inconvenience, we regret it. However, we had to make sure of the precise decision of the Holy Office. I did not go to Rome solely for this matter, but you may rest assured that while there I sought advice from the highest sources possible. The decision has been announced. It is my unpleasant task to inform you and carry out to the letter the ruling that has been made.

"You are excommunicated on the grounds of persistent violation of your vow of obedience. Once a week since coming to Santa Bella, you have had consultations with a variety of church officials, including physicians, pastors—young priests and old priests—and the psychiatrist. The reports from all of these men add up to one thing: you are unfit to be a priest in the Holy Church; you do not know the meaning of obedience. In order to satisfy my own mind and conscience I now ask you to give me clearly your interpretation of obedience."

I remained silent for a long while. Then I swallowed hard and said, "Father, the enlightened conscience, not the Pope, is man's supreme court."

At this point the old man began to weep, at first softly, with the tears barely showing in his eyes. Then the weeping shook his frail body. At last he wiped his eyes and excused himself.

"My son," he said, "the Holy Father does not excommunicate you, the Church does not excommunicate you, I do not excommunicate you—you have excommunicated yourself."

He continued, "In light of the many challenges to the authority of the Church you will be made an example. It must be made clear to priests in Holland, England, France, Germany, and the United States that in the matter of faith and morals there is still supreme authority in the Holy Church. Priests such as yourself have become the Holy Father's crown of thorns."

Then the old man with quivering voice explained to me the terms of excommunication. I would be permitted to attend

126

Mass but not to take Communion. Under no circumstances could I ever be reinstated as a priest. By a series of penitential acts, I might someday become eligible to receive the sacraments, but *never again could I function as a priest.* Until the day when I have paid in full for my sins, I am a public sinner with the wrath of God resting upon my head.

The old man rose and I rose. We faced each other. He did not shake my hand, but took me in his arms as a father would a wayward son, and kept repeating, "My son, my son, my son, would God that I had died for you." That's the way I left the Father Superior's office.

I have since learned a little about the background of the old man. His name is Patrick Mulligan, his home near Dublin not more than twenty miles from mine. In Ireland, he went to the same grammar school as I, and by a strange coincidence also to St. Joseph's, the very seminary from which I graduated. I suppose in more ways than one Father Mulligan considered me his son.

When you write, address your letter to General Delivery, San Diego. I will try to keep you informed.

Sean

SECTION EIGHT

Something New Under the Heavens

Dear Sean,

It was a relief to receive your letter and to learn that you are all right. At least you are alive and functioning. I know you are torn by the hierarchy's decision, but believe me, for you life is not over. A man with your abilities, your faith in God and compassion for people, will find a useful place to work. Of course, I have mixed feelings about your separation from the priesthood. On the one hand, I am sorry because of the anguish and disappointment it has brought you. On the other hand, I feel that without the multiple restrictions of the Church you are likely to do more good.

I hope Tim's offer is still open to you. Going to Hong Kong would of course mean that Grace and I would not be likely to see you again. But to work with students in the formative years of their lives would be a great privilege. If Tim has filled the position in Latin studies, perhaps he will have another opening. I can see all manner of possibilities for you. The main thing at this moment is not to lose your grip on yourself. *You are Sean O'Malley, a wonderful human being. Nothing must destroy that.*

Dan Brewster, the young Briar Wood lawyer, took me to lunch yesterday. He is still excited about the new church at Bay Ridge. They now have sixty adult members and are more involved with the community than ever. Their current battle is with the school board, which has been dragging its feet on desegregation. Dr. Breaker, with a committee of housewives in the church, has also been assisting on an upgraded program of free medical and dental services for school children. This same committee sent representatives to the state capital to register protests against two anachronistic laws: one that prohibits interracial marriage and another which denies the right of a woman to have an abortion.

From the way Dan talks, their church must be an exciting adventure. Sunday morning services of worship are certainly not according to a standard Presbyterian order of service! There is singing and instrumental music, spontaneous prayers by members of the congregation, and readings from both the Scriptures and contemporary literature. During the service, members of the congregation describe their concerns and their involvement. Last Sunday the committee, having just returned from the capital, gave their personal "testimonies" concerning their protests. The service is concluded with a brief message by one of the members.

Thursday evenings are devoted to education (they do not have a *Sunday* school). A simple supper is prepared and served by the members, men and women. Following supper, classes for children and adults are held until about nine o'clock. In these classes the people are attempting to discover how to make the message of the Bible meaningful in today's problems. Dan said to me, "This is where we need you. Neither John Breaker nor myself nor any of the members feel qualified as a Bible or theological teacher. We need someone with your training, but especially someone with your point of view." It is an inspiration to me that these young people have organized a church and are performing a ministry without the help of any minister, secretary, board, or agency!

Dan explained something about their church which will make the presbytery flip if and when they ever apply for membership. They intend to have a genuine ministry of the laity, not a phony lay ministry. Preachers have long agonized over a clergy-directed church. "What we need is more good laymen," they have said. By that they mean more experienced and more dedicated churchmen who will bring their business and financial experience to the administrative aspects of the church. Dan says that by a ministry of the laity his group means just that. Laymen and laywomen will preside at the Communion service, they will baptize babies, conduct funerals, and with permission of the state, perform wedding services. Weddings will be performed in connection with the Sunday morning service. There will be no special dress for the bride or groom and no parading in and out. The bride and groom will simply stand during the service and repeat their vows before the congregation. There will also be a special committee on personal problems—a member in trouble may go to certain designated members of the congregation and "talk it out." Those members will be under the same vow of confidence as if they had been ordained.

Dan said that if I would come and help them there would be no pressure to recruit new members, no visiting of prospects, no visiting "dropouts," and *no fund-raising.* I would be their leader, their teacher, their advisor on things pertaining to the Bible and to the Christian faith. Then he told me something that made my head swim: "We expect the leader of our congregation to hold a job in the community just like the rest of us. It may be a part-time job, but it will be a job 'in the world.'"

Sean, I know that with your sacramental commitment to ordination this idea does not appeal to you—it probably sounds too much like a wild-sect movement—but I'll be damned if it doesn't make sense to me.

However, I quit pussyfooting around and finally told Dan that I could not possibly accept their invitation. I gave him no specific reason, but you know as well as I that part of my problem is financial. I simply could not make it—besides, my retirement program would go down the drain.

We shook hands, Dan wished me well and we parted friends. To be trusted and wanted by such a group of exciting young people is the greatest honor of my life.

Tom

P.S. Heard from Tom, Jr. this morning, and we are relieved and overjoyed! His views on Vietnam are changing. He will complete his tour by the end of July and reenter Princeton in September. He has another year. I'll have to borrow to see him through, but I'll do it gladly.

The Next Step

Dear Tom,

I am writing to you from San Francisco, where I am likely to remain. As you know, centers have arisen all over the country for the counseling and assistance of priests and nuns who for any reason have broken with the Church. There is one in St. Petersburg, Florida, one in Chicago, another in New York, but one of the most active agencies is in San Francisco.

The place is known as "The Next Step." Up to the present time they have assisted hundreds of priests (and lately a number of Protestant clergymen) who are finding it difficult to get located in "civilian" life. I was helped by a conference with a professor of sociology at the University of San Francisco, who is associated with this outfit. He is interested in dropouts, especially from the priesthood, and is currently making an exhaustive study. He tells me that my case is unique. The vast majority of priests who leave the priesthood do so because of the celibacy restriction.

The professor asked me three questions: "Do you intend to marry?" I replied, "No, I shall remain celibate the rest of my life."

Then a direct question: "Have you ever experienced overt or nonovert homosexual activity?"

I replied, "Never—I would be repulsed by such practices."

Then: "Are you sexless, without the power of the sex drive?"

I replied, "No—I am not. There is such a thing as self-control and sublimation." I did not feel obligated to tell him about the relation that developed between Marie and myself.

The professor was interested in my background in Latin American studies and is quite sure he can help me find a teaching position in the States, perhaps on the college or

university level. I told him the details of my activity with the
Center in Puerto Rico, of my arrest and conviction and expulsion from the country. He laughed and said that this would
be my strongest recommendation.

There are three additional people on the staff of "The Next
Step," and I was interviewed by two of them—an ex-priest
and an ex-nun. They appeared eager to help. The priest, a
former Jesuit, is now married and has a home on the outskirts
of San Francisco. He insisted that I stay with him until I get
my bearings. He feels that by fall I should have several teaching offers. I am presently at his house and will be here for a
few days. His wife is a lawyer but is extremely feminine—not
beautiful, but a person who radiates warmth and charm.

I like San Francisco very much. It would be nice to live
here. I will let you know within a few days.

Sean

Handling Life's Second-Bests

Dear Tom,

You may have written to me at the San Francisco address.
However, I did not stay there, and though I was offered a
position teaching at San Francisco State, I turned it down.
Yesterday I returned to San Diego, where I will be for a
couple of weeks. I wired Tim that if he still needed me in his
school I would accept the position in September. He sent me
a thousand dollars, so at the moment I have no financial

obligations. Somehow I feel that the farther I get from Santa Bella and all that it stands for, the easier it will be for me to accept my new status. I will try to lose myself in teaching teen-age classes and rid myself of the strange feeling that I am no longer a priest.

While I was in San Francisco, I received a letter from Mary my older sister. Upon hearing from the village priest that I had been excommunicated, my aged and invalid mother gave up and died. My father, eighty-four, is now at the point of death but Mary says it would be better not to try to see him before he dies or even attend his funeral. She holds me responsible for our mother's death and Father's critical illness. No good would come from my going back to Ireland now. But she promised to let me know when the end comes.

I regret very much that I shall not see you and Grace before leaving for Hong Kong, but the time is now short. Please be assured that I shall hold you and your family in my prayers.

Sean

P.S. My chief reason for not visiting the East is not the Bishop or the Church—that's over. I would not trust myself to get near enough to see Marie and talk to her.

A Priest Forever

Dear Tom,

This letter is being written from a migrant camp in California's San Joaquin Valley, not too far from Fresno. At last I am settled. It is possible that your last several letters have not caught up with me, for I have been on the move. Now, thank

God, I am settled. I have found the light and I have found myself.

From the time I left Santa Bella nearly two months ago, I have been in a state of shock and disbelief. I surely have not been myself. This new, rootless existence is so foreign to me that I did not know how to adjust to it. By temperament, I have always found it easy to locate in one community and remain there for a considerable stretch of time—more than ten years in Briar Wood, five years in Puerto Rico. Stripped of my vocation and dismissed from the retreat center, I knew nothing better to do than to wander up and down California. Never having been west of the Mississippi, I have no close friends here. I traveled incognito. On buses or hitchhiking, I talked to as many people as possible. What I learned from such contacts was more than an education. It has brought a new center to my life.

My visit to San Francisco and "The Next Step" was fruitful. I found people there eager to help, and I was offered a teaching position, but for some reason I could not accept it.

The decision to accept Tim's offer was made in good faith, but I sensed that it was a wrong decision. It was settling for something less than what I am called to do—an attempt to shape the rest of my life around second choices. I finally wrote Tim that I could not, after all, accept his kind and generous offer and returned most of the $1,000. The rest I shall repay before the end of the year. I hope he will be able to understand.

It has now been more than two weeks since I wrote you. After making the decision not to go to Hong Kong, I took a bus trip up the Valley to Stockton and then south to Fresno. Why did I choose to make this trip? What force was moving me to this end? Chance? Coincidence? Or God? I prefer to believe it was the loving Spirit of God. The trip through the Valley with the great mountains on either side is majestic and inspiring. Everywhere there is beauty, charm, affluence, and prosperity. I was reminded of my beloved Puerto Rico—the

Garden of Eden. Beauty and charm everywhere, except in the camps of the migrants, the "wetbacks." These are mostly Mexican migrant laborers with a few Negro and Indian families. Once again I was reminded of Puerto Rico. In this valley wetbacks by the thousands live in conditions not fit for an animal. In many ways their fate is worse than that of tenant farmers in Puerto Rico. To be sure, they are paid more, but inflationary prices in California are the highest in the nation. The cost of food, clothing, rent, travel, medical services, etc., is more than double that in the Commonwealth, or indeed any other place in the United States.

Not only so, but the workers, many of whom do not speak English, are often mistreated and exploited by their own leaders, who act in collusion with employers.

Last Saturday, late in the afternoon, I walked to a migrant camp several miles from the town of Modera. I had seen a crudely printed handbill saying that a man by the name of Miguel Cervantes was to speak, and that he was calling upon the people to form a union. A great crowd had gathered to hear the speaker, who stood on top of several crates. He was small and wiry, and had a charismatic spirit. Speaking through an amplifying system, his voice was both exciting and at times subdued. He was calling for a strike against the owners of the massive vineyards in San Joaquin Valley. Cervantes spent considerable time explaining to the workers the degree of their exploitation, the reasons why they were economically deprived, and what they could do about their plight. He then mentioned the name of a great U.S. Senator (not from California) who had publically expressed sympathy for the workers. He further announced that this Senator would be in the Valley to speak to the people within the month.

My clothes were somewhat tattered—I was easily taken to be one of the workers. And for a while, so real was the situation, I thought of myself as a wetback grape-picker. I edged my way through the crowd so as to get a better look at the

135

speaker. At this point, near the end of his speech, Cervantes' voice became hard and his eyes narrowed as he described the efforts of certain Mexican leaders to prevent the workers from organizing. He charged them (one of them by name) with deceiving their own people and being paid by the owners, who would resort to any means to prevent the migrants from forming a union with power.

Cervantes spoke to his people: "We shall overcome—no longer will we be machines for greedy people, no longer will our children go without food, medical services, and education—no longer will we live in shacks and hovels without sanitation—we shall overcome!"

He completed his speech with a word of warning to the owners. His workers would strike, and they would strike during the harvest. Recently, $7 million worth of pineapples in Hawaii were left to rot in the fields during a sixty-one-day strike. His closing remark was, "We have little to lose except our rags and our hovels—owners of the fields have everything to lose."

That was late Saturday afternoon.

Sunday morning I attended early Mass in Fresno—I have not missed Sunday Mass since leaving Santa Bella. I am more a Catholic now than I have ever been. I sat in the rear of the church and listened to the priest intone the words of the Mass. Suddenly, as with St. Paul, a light flashed in my brain and I heard the voice of Christ, "Sean O'Malley, you are a priest, you are a priest forever."

In that moment I recalled (the memory is tricky) certain words from the Council of Trent, session XXIII, canon 4, which we were required to memorize before ordination. The words literally burned into my brain: "Let him be anathema who dares say that he who was once a priest can again become a layman." And from the New Testament, "Thou art a priest forever."

I arose in the middle of the Mass and made my way to a small park and under the shade of a great tree I tried to come to grips with the idea that had come to me.

Was I still a priest?

Could anyone ever take the priesthood away from me?

I once answered the call of Christ to the religious vocation and I have been ordained. I believe the Creeds, every word of them. I believe in God the Maker of heaven and earth, I believe in Jesus Christ, His Son, I believe in the Holy Ghost who proceeds from Father and Son, I believe in the Holy Catholic Church, I believe in the goodness, purity and saint-hood of the Holy Virgin, I believe in the validity of the seven sacraments and that God's grace is mediated to needy people through the ministry of those who have heard and answered the call to the religious life.

When we were students completing the requirements for ordination, one truth above all others was drilled into us. That was the affirmation that the sacraments in the hands of a priest of God confer grace upon the people *ex opere operato.* This means that they do not depend for their validity upon the emotional or mental condition of the priest (he may be drunk or insane—God forbid). Validity does not depend on the priest's moral life, character, or even on his private be-liefs. When an ordained priest, though wicked and unbeliev-ing, yet intending to do what the Church does, observes the appointed forms, the people need not fear that grace will not be transmitted to them. The priest is simply an instrument (frail) in the hands of the Giver, Christ Jesus. So the phrase *ex opere operato* means "operating on its own," and it has been extremely helpful to me in the decision I have made.

I went to see Miguel Cervantes, told him my background, including the various incidents in Puerto Rico. And I further told him that I wanted to join him and his workers in the great struggle of the San Joaquin Valley. Cervantes, a deeply religious man, is married to a Protestant, a divorced woman, and is therefore outside the Church. I explained that I wanted to be a worker with the workers, at their wages and hours, but I also wanted to be a priest to them. As such I shall

137

minister to all who come my way, many of whom have been excluded from the Church for the same reason as Miguel. I shall baptize their babies, in the name of the Father, the Son and the Holy Ghost. I shall confirm their children, hear confessions, grant absolution and comfort the bereaved. I shall say Mass and offer the Body of Christ to all who come. I shall pray for the dying and anoint the dead, and I shall give the blessing of the Church to those who seek it.

There will be no building called "the church." The church will be the suffering people of God who care for each other. Mass will be offered in a worker's shack or on top of a jeep. I have carried with me the kit (an authentic altar stone) which I used in the slums and fields of Puerto Rico. I have taken off street clothes, and now again I wear the robe of sackcloth. A rope with three knots in it is tied about my waist. These knots are to me precious symbols of my dedication to the priesthood. They stand for poverty, chastity, and obedience. I shall know personally the *poverty* of California's wetbacks. I settled the *chastity* question a long time ago, and with the satisfactions of my new work I shall have no trouble at that point. Above all, I shall be *obedient*—obedient to the Christ who called me into the priesthood.

You may write to me in care of post office Box #10 in Modera. If you ever come this way, go directly to the headquarters of the Migrant Workers' Union in Modera. Miguel has someone there twenty-four hours a day. Simply ask for the priest of the Valley and you will be told in what vineyards or fields he is working.

With every good wish, and hoping that someday we shall see each other again, I am

As always,

Sean O'Malley, a priest forever

A Funny Thing Happened at the Banquet

Dear Sean,

What great, wonderful, blessed news!

I knew you would eventually find the place of service where you could do the most good. It almost makes a heretic like myself believe in the guidance of God.

Hold your breath. Grace and I are coming to see you. I received the doctor of divinity degree at Claymore last Monday night. Frankly, I feel highly honored. Friday night of this past week I was jolted with the surprise of my life. As I told you, the Smoketown Community Center and Presbyterian Chapel have succeeded in spite of local excesses of white racism and black power. The center is still efficiently directed by the same young woman—graduate of Howard. The chapel was taken into the presbytery and is now a full-blown Presbyterian church, the membership about half-white and half-black—what a witness and testimony in this day of irrational attitudes among the races!

The mortgage at the new church was recently paid off. Several of the elders and deacons from my church along with elders and deacons in the Smoketown Church decided to have a celebration at the Briar Wood Hotel. We were to have a big banquet, officials from the synod would be present, brief speeches were to be made by leaders in both churches as well as the local presbytery.

I soon discovered there was another reason for the celebration. Hank Bowers and several other men in my church, along with Dr. Arch Thomas, the Negro obstetrician, banded together and planned the entire banquet—not in celebration of a new church coming into the presbytery, but in my honor! As I walked into the dining room, Grace—who had been in on the whole deal—rushed from the dais, threw her arms around me and kissed me. A band began to play, and the crowd sang, "Tom Jones—for he's a jolly good fellow, he's a jolly good fellow," etc.

Dumfounded, I was led to the speaker's table, Grace by my side. The master of ceremonies called on Father Giovonni, your successor, to pronounce the invocation. I was too overcome to hear his prayer or know what was happening. A very good young tenor from the Smoketown choir sang "The Impossible Dream," following which the Mayor of Briar Wood delivered a eulogy entitled "Tom Jones, Briar Wood's Man of the Year."

Several speeches followed. These included, "Tom Jones, the Community Leader," "Tom Jones, the Church Leader," "Tom Jones, Everybody's Friend," "Tom Jones, the Conscience of Briar Wood." The last talk, on "Conscience," was delivered by a black man, chairman of the board of elders of the Smoketown Church.

By this time I was overcome and visibly shaken, but the icing on the cake came at the end of the program. Julian (the rascal was present—he has accepted his old job at Beth Israel) came forward to say that the men of both churches, my church and Smoketown, knowing of the deep friendship between him and myself, had asked him to make an important announcement. He began by saying that everyone in Briar Wood knew how much time and labor Tom Jones had put into the community center and the chapel. "If it had not been for our honored guest, both projects would have long since died." Julian then dropped the bombshell: the new Presbyterian Church in Smoketown is being named the Thomas Emerson Jones Presbyterian Church!

What could I say!

I was speechless.

You know, if no one else does, my awful impatience with "memorial" churches—have I not lived with one for more than twelve years? But what was I to do? I got to my feet, fumbled with words, and with as much sincerity as possible accepted the honor which had been heaped upon me.

Then Grace kissed me again and the crowd stood and sang again, "For he's a jolly good fellow!"

Just before the benediction, the chairman of our board of elders announced that our church had granted an eight week vacation—July and August—to the pastor and his wife, along with a handsome purse.

So California, here we come! To meet again with my friend Sean O'Malley will be for me the event of the year.

Tom

There's More To Come

Dear Sean,

Weeks have passed since Grace and I made the memorable trip to the San Joaquin Valley. I regret that I have not written but things have been happening so fast that my life is in a constant whirl. Tom came home and reentered Princeton. He is a different person, and at last we can communicate with each other. (Virginia is married, lives in Manhattan and is receiving a number of exciting acting opportunities. Jim is a freshman at the University of Mississippi, still knocking heads together on the football field and still crusading to keep "the blacks from taking over.")

I write to say that the visit with you shook me to the depths of my life; I was expecting to find someone living a grubby existence and adapting to a makeshift priestly arrangement. But what did I find? A human being radiant in the confidence that he is doing God's work on earth as a worker-priest! On

141

the trip back across the country Grace and I were consumed by one topic of conversation: is there any way, is there anything we can do, to bring such meaning and satisfaction to our own lives and ministry?

Well, to make a long story short, by the time we reached Briar Wood we had made up our minds. I resigned my church and took the position of "leader" of the little congregation at Bay Ridge. I explained the situation to the presbytery, and to my surprise they gave me permission to take up duties on special assignment. I also explained that within a few months the Bay Ridge congregation would likely apply for membership in the presbytery, not as a mission station needing money but as a full-fledged church. The presbytery must be prepared to reject or accept this unorthodox group of young people, nearly all of whom were brought up in traditional Presbyterian churches. If the presbytery should refuse them membership, what do you suppose could be the grounds of refusal? The statement of faith? I think not. The new confession of faith of the United Presbyterian Church U.S.A. is more than acceptable to the congregation—they have already voted it as their guide in faith and practice! What then? This new church will be rejected because it is insisting on a genuine "ministry of the laity which is nothing less than the pure ministry (priesthood) of all believers." Laymen will not simply act in administrative matters or as adjuncts to the ordained clergy, but will participate in all matters temporal and spiritual.

In the sect of Jehovah's Witnesses baptized believers are ordained ministers; thus ordination in a sense is put on a pedestal. In the original Quaker movement, which has greatly influenced my thought at this point, there was no such thing as ordination. Every man was responsible for his own gifts and for doing his own thing as he was guided by the Inner Light. The difference between the Bay Ridge community and a Quaker meeting is that in the Bay Ridge community, strong theological presuppositions support and

142

motivate Christian activity. Furthermore, in this new church, though the "leader" need not be an ordained clergyman, he must be trained in philosophy, theology and the Bible, as well as all the liberal arts.

The position of the Roman Catholic Church regarding ordination as a separated and special life is the only logical and consistent one. In the Roman Church a man is ordained, set apart, and given certain powers and privileges not entrusted to other people. Few, if any, Protestant denominations interpret ordination in this manner. Even in the Episcopal Church, which places such emphasis on apostolic succession, there are only a limited number of things a layman cannot do, and in a pinch my guess is a layman's ministry at these points would be effective and as pleasing to God as if performed by an absent rector. Thus, in most Protestant denominations a man is ordained, but he is *not* granted distinctive powers. He alone (except in denominations such as Disciples and Baptist) may preside at Communion, but in no way are the elements or the people changed because of his presence. The Protestant minister may listen to a person's confession, but his ministry is not that of granting absolution. It is to respond with insight and kindness to the person's problems, as would be the case with any compassionate person, lay or clerical. The minister may offer a prayer for a sick person, but his prayer is no more effective than that of any believing person. The minister may conduct a funeral service, but he does nothing for the living or the dead that any member of the church could not do. The same is true of weddings. In other words most Protestant denominations set the minister apart and give him the burdens of ordination (including an intolerable public image) without granting him unique powers and privileges.

In the eyes of the Bay Ridge congregation my ordination means little. I am not separated or in any way different from any of the members. In other words there is no double life or double standard. By virtue of training, my principal pastoral

143

duties involve teaching. Like the rabbi of old, I am a resource person in the areas of biblical and theological interpretation. Of course, I will take my turn serving on various committees such as counseling, funerals, weddings, education, worship, budget, political action, antipoverty, etc.

We made the break and have never been happier. We have found the light. Our fears about financial matters have disappeared. After all, we are children, products of the most disastrous financial depression of all time, and as with most people of our generation, we have been obsessed with the level of income, savings, insurance, sick benefits, retirement, etc. Now that we have taken the plunge we have also taken the risks even as other members of the Bay Ridge congregation. For the first time in our married life we are not living in a manse—Grace, Gail, and I are living in a small two-bedroom apartment and we like it. We feel like real human beings, not a family set apart.

The congregation pays me a small stipend, and I also have a job at Briar Wood's branch of ETC as part-time personnel director. I work from one in the afternoon to six, five days a week. The rest of my time is devoted to the church. Grace is teaching school, fourth grade, and we are meeting our obligations, including keeping Tom in Princeton.

There are two important results from this new minister-laity arrangement. I have unlimited freedom to teach in love the truth as I understand it. Members have unlimited freedom to agree or disagree in love with anything I say. This type of freedom is a sacred trust, it is like clean, fresh air to a smothering man. So long as a pastor is wholly dependent upon a congregation (elders, deacons, vestry) for his livelihood, he is not free in the truest sense of the word. He may function, but he will always be conscious of this dependency.

The second factor is equally important. Members of this small congregation are not fooling themselves. They know they are not exhausting their Christian responsibilities by witnessing to the power of love through an organization, no

FINDING THE LIGHT

matter how active it may be. They are keenly aware of the necessity of being deployed in the world in the manner of the Apostle Paul, who worked as a tentmaker. Taking the job at ETC, like other members I am now "in the world" in a real way, perhaps the only way that matters. The separated clergy cannot escape the separated life. No matter how many clubs he joins or how many community functions he participates in, he is really not in the workaday world until he becomes, as you have, and I hope I shall, an integral part of the working community. This is the best of both worlds—the worker-priest, the worker-minister.

Good luck, God bless you, until we meet again.

Tom

70 71 72 73 10 9 8 7 6 5 4 3 2 1